IDF ARMOURED VEHICLES

Tracked Armour of the Modern Israeli Defense Forces (IDF)
Gepanzerte Kettenfahrzeuge der Modernen Israelischen Armee

Soeren Suenkler
& Marsh Gelbart

Editor´s Note

In the past decades the Israeli Army, and especially the Israeli Armoured Corps, has earned a reputation of being the best-trained and best-equipped force for territorial defence in the world. However, unlike many other nations the Israeli Government has never disclosed substantial information or pictorial confirmation about the vehicles in active use. Thus, there have been not many chances to publish a photographical survey in that extent as shown here, especially in the recent years.
The main focus of this exceptional publication is therefore not an encyclopedic approach, but to provide the enthusiast in Israeli military vehicles an overview about the main armoured vehicle types in use today, and with a strong emphasis on many of the unique technical details of the Israeli conversions and upgrades.

All photographs credited (Author) have been taken by Soeren Suenkler in 2005.
Jochen Vollert, Publisher, October 2006

Anmerkungen des Herausgebers

In den vergangenen Jahrzehnten hat sich die Israelische Armee, und besonders die Israelische Panzertruppe, als die am besten ausgebildete und am besten ausgestattete Kraft in der territorialen Verteidigung etabliert. Im Gegensatz zu anderen modernen Landstreitkräften hat die Israelische Armee jedoch nur sehr eingeschränkt wesentliche Informationen oder bildliche Darstellungen ihrer Fahrzeuge der breiten Öffentlichkeit zugänglich gemacht. Somit gab es besonders in den letzten Jahren nur sehr wenige Möglichkeiten, eine ausführliche Publikation zum Thema herauszubringen.
Aus diesem Grunde liegt der Schwerpunkt dieses vorliegenden Buches nicht auf einer enzyklopädischen Abhandlung, sondern auf der Darstellung der wichtigsten gepanzerten Kettenfahrzeuge der Israelischen Armee, besonders im Hinblick auf technische Details der einmaligen israelischen Umbauten und Modernisierungsmaßnahmen.

Alle Fotos, die mit der Quelle (Author) versehen sind, wurden von Soeren Suenkler 2005 aufgenommen.
Jochen Vollert, Herausgeber, Oktober 2006

Acknowledgements

To gather the photographs for this publication has not been easy, despite my experiences as a combat correspondent and photographer. Without the following persons and institutions and their decisive support, it would not have been possible. Thanks to: Marsh Gelbart for his expertise in identifying the vehicles. Katrin Schulz for her pre-research, Helena Moshe for the organisation in Israel, Yiftach Ofek for his support with photos, Adi of the IDF Spokesperson Unit for the permissions and Adi of the IDF Southern Command for the support in Beer Sheva. Not to forget the many soldiers and members of the IDF Spokesperson Unit and Israeli Army - who must remain unnamed.
Soeren Suenkler, October 2006

Danksagung

Die Fotos für dieses Werk zusammenzutragen war keine leichte Aufgabe, trotz meiner Erfahrungen als Krisenreporter und wehrtechnischer Fotojournalist. Deshalb gilt mein besonderer Dank folgenden Personen und Institutionen für deren entscheidende Unterstützung:
Marsh Gelbart für seine Identifikation der Fahrzeuge. Katrin Schulze für die Vorredaktion, Helena Moshe für die Organisation in Israel, Yiftach Ofek für die bildliche Unterstützung, Adi von der IDF Spokesperson Unit für die Genehmigungen und Adi vom IDF Südkommando für die Unterstützung in Beer Sheba. Im weiteren einer Vielzahl von Unterstützern innerhalb der israelischen Armee, die leider ungenannt bleiben müssen.
Soeren Suenkler, Oktober 2006

ISBN 3-936519-03-X

Verlag Jochen Vollert - Tankograd Publishing
Wilhelmstr. 2 b, 91054 Erlangen, Germany

Content / *Inhaltsangabe*

Chapter / *Kapitel*	Page / *Seite*

(Author)

The Armoured Units of the Israeli Army
Gepanzerte Einheiten der Israelischen Armee

The Modern Israeli Armoured Forces Today

The history of the State of Israel is dominated by conflict and war with its neighbours. Israel was born in war. Its continuous existence, struggle for political survival and fight for acceptance within the international community have proved equally dramatic. Despite all political efforts for peace in the Middle East, the Israeli Army, IDF – Israeli Defence Forces, remains the guarantor of the security and survival of the Israeli people and their state.

Besides fielding one of the most modern and capable air forces in the world, the Israeli armed forces are equipped with highly trained and well-equipped mechanised units in the land forces. These comprise of light and mobile infantry units, armoured units and combat engineers. In addition the corps of artillery plays a vital role.

A detailed description of the organisation of the modern Israeli Army is currently impossible. This fact is based on one hand on the tremendous level of secrecy within the IDF, on the other hand on the highly flexible battle-group style of organisation. Classical larger formations seem virtually not to exist on a long-term basis – the constant threat of conflict with ever-changing scenarios demand a highly adaptable organisational scheme in combination with the limited resources available inside the country. Despite this demanding environment, the IDF is the most capable and combat ready force in the Middle East, superior to any regular Arab army in the region.

The key to success in land battle definitely were the armoured formations. Independent sources claim that "no Israeli soldier has to walk into battle on his own feet" and that the number of armoured vehicles available includes (active + war reserve)* approx. 3,900 main battle tanks, 8,200 other armoured vehicles, 996 artillery self-propelled guns and 190 multiple launch rocket systems. Aside of many imported weapons and vehicles, often locally adapted to better meet with Israeli requirements, the IDF also runs its own main battle tank programme – the Merkava.

In addition to the equipment available, the IDF consists of highly trained and motivated personnel. Although the professional core of the Israeli army is small, its numbers are swelled by conscripts and by the calling up of the reserves; those soldiers who have completed their National Service.

As of 2005 * the total strength of the Israeli Army theoretically consisted of 105,000 – 175,000 (plus 380,000 – 600,000 reserve) in 3 Corps, 12 armoured divisions (each consisting of 2-3 armoured brigades, 1 mechanised brigade and 1 artillery brigade), 4 mechanised divisions, 9

Die modernen gepanzerten israelischen Streitkräfte heute

Die moderne Geschichte Israels ist eine lange Abfolge von Konflikten und Kriegen. Dramatisch ist nicht nur die Entstehung dieses jungen Landes, sondern auch sein politischer Überlebenskampf und die folgende Integration in die Weltgemeinschaft. Trotz aller politischer Bemühung um Frieden in dieser Region, bleibt das israelische Militär, die IDF (Israel Defense Forces, in Hebräisch „Zahal" genannt) das Rückgrat israelischer Außen- und Innenpolitik. Geographisch eingezwängt zwischen potentiellen Gegnern, bedeutet für Israel die Existenz eigener, gut ausgerüsteter Streitkräfte das eigene politische und geographische Überleben.

Schwerpunkt der IDF sind, neben einer modernen und gut funktionierenden Luftwaffe, die mittleren und schweren mechanisierten Verbände des Heeres. Diese bestehen aus leichten Infanterieverbänden, Einheiten der Panzertruppe und Kampfpionieren. Ebenso sind zahlreiche Artillerieeinheiten in diese Gliederung integriert.

Eine reine schematische und exemplarische Darstellung der mechanisierten IDF Verbände ist aus verschiedenen Gründen fast unmöglich. Zum einem liegt über der Zahal immer der Schleier der Geheimhaltung, zum anderen sind diese Einheiten in ihrer Struktur sehr dynamisch - es scheint tatsächlich wenige feste Großverbände im klassischen Sinne zu geben. Diese Tatsache basiert auf verschiedenen Fakten: Es herrscht ein dauerhafter Konflikt, an den die Verbandsstrukturen permanent angepasst werden und durch den Mangel an Ressourcen wird ständig improvisiert. Trotzdem ist die IDF die wohl schlagkräftigste Armee im Nahen Osten und allen arabischen Nachbarn militärisch überlegen. Dies liegt in der starken Ausprägung der mechanisierten Verbände und in der dynamischen Panzertruppe. Unabhängigen Recherchen zu Folge, muss kein israelischer Soldat zu Fuß gehen und die Zahl der gepanzerten Fahrzeuge übersteigt mit (aktiv + Kriegsreserve *) ca. 3.900 Kampfpanzern, 8.200 anderen gepanzerten Fahrzeugen, 996 Selbstfahrlafetten der Artillerie und 190 Geschosswerfern ein Vielfaches einzelner arabischer Streitkräfte. Neben einer Vielzahl älterer, aber ständig vor Ort modifizierter Importe, verfügt Israel auch über ein eigenes, recht erfolgreiches Kampfpanzerprojekt - den Merkava. Zudem besteht die IDF aus militärisch exzellent ausgebildetem Personal.

Die Schlagkraft der modernen israelischen Landstreitkräfte schlüsselt sich mit einer theoretischen Stärke von (Stand 2005*) 105.000 - 175.000 Soldaten (plus 380.000 - 600.000 Reservisten im Kriegsfall) auf in 3 Korps, 12 gepanzerte Divisionen (bestehend aus jeweils 2 - 3 Panzerbrigaden, 1 mechanisierten Brigade und 1 Artilleriebrigade), 4

(Author)

(Author)

mechanised brigades and 4 airborne brigades. All figures include war reserve and are unconfirmed.

The spearhead of IDF land forces is the **armoured corps** supported by highly mechanised units and supply units. Currently the existence of only three active armoured brigades is confirmed: 188th Barak, 401st Ikvot Habarzel and the 7th Hativa Sheva Brigade. These would fight alongside the four large infantry brigades: Givati, Golani, Nahal and T´zanhanim. As of 2005 the Israeli armoured corps fields the following quantities and vehicle-types*: approx. 1,100 Merkava 2/3, 400 Merkava 4, 1,800 M60 MAGACH variants, 200 M48 MAGACH variants as well as 260 captured and converted T-54/55/62 tanks designated as TIRAN 4/5/6. Most of the latter are mothballed as war reserve or have meanwhile been converted into Achzarit armoured infantry carriers. In addition 300 Centurion main battle tanks are still listed. It seems, however, that these have now almost completely been converted into Puma armoured engineer vehicles. Interestingly enough no Merkava 1 tanks can be found in that list - all of these have already been upgraded.

Combat engineers, a role that has grown in importance for the IDF in recent years, can either operate independently or be directly integrated at a company level, within battle groups. The engineers and the **infantry** are equipped with specialised armoured vehicles such as 400 Nagmashot/Puma and 200 Achzarit. Around 5,500 M113 armoured personnel carriers are fielded. Although the infantry are the prime users, a wide number of variants are used by other IDF combat arms. Interestingly enough specialised variants of M2/M3 half tracks of WWII vintage are part of the war reserve!*

The **artillery** primarily fields the M109 self-propelled howitzer and is subdivided into three active brigades. The backbone of the IDF's artillery is the M109 self-propelled howitzer. Most of the 600 in service have been upgraded, initially to the Rochev (Rider) standard and then to the improved Doher (Galloper). As of 2005 the types in active service or mothballed comprised of 140 175mm M107 Romach, 36 203mm M110, 120 155mm L-33 and a total of 600 155mm M109. The self propelled artillery is backed by 460 towed artillery pieces as well as 190 multiple-launch rocket systems (the bulk of captured Soviet origin). The most potent of the rocket launchers are the 48 U.S. supplied MLRS.

Aside of these major combat units quite a large number a smaller **specialised units**, often mixed and independent as well as mechanised exist and are often supported by an undisclosed variety of special forces (Sayeret).

A permanent order of battle and organisation on divisional level could not be verified up to the present day. However, inside sources speak of at least one division for the **military sectors** Gaza, Eilat, Golan, Galilee, Judea and Samaria. The largest tactical element seems to be the independent mixed brigade.

mechanisierten Divisionen, 9 mechanisierten Brigaden und 4 Luftlandebrigaden*. Alle Angaben inklusive voller Mobilisierung / Kriegsreserve.

Speerspitze der Zahal ist nach wie vor die **Panzertruppe** und eine Vielzahl von mechanisierten Begleit-, Kampf- und Unterstützungsverbänden. Die Panzertruppe überlebt Dank unregelmäßiger Importe, ständiger Improvisation, Ideenreichtum und unglaublicher Eigendynamik. Bis heute ist nur die Existenz von drei aktiven gepanzerten Brigaden bestätigt: Die 188. Barak, die 401. Ikvot Habarzel und die 7. Hativa Sheva Brigade. Diese kämpfen im Verbund mit den vier großen Infanteriebrigaden: Givati, Golani, Nahal und T´zanhanim. Die Ausstattung der Panzertruppe besteht mit Stand 2005 * aus 1.100 Merkava 2/3 und 400 Merkava 4, sowie 1.800 M60 MAGACH in verschiedenen Ausführungen, rund 200 M48 MAGACH sowie 260 erbeuteten und modifizierten T-54/T-55/T-62 Kampfpanzern TIRAN 4/5/6, die jedoch meist eingemottet oder bereits zu Achzarit umgebaut wurden. Die teilweise im Bestand geführten noch rund 300 Kampfpanzer Centurion sind bereits fast vollständig zu Puma-Kampffahrzeugen umgebaut. Interessanterweise finden sich keine Merkava 1 Kampfpanzer mehr - diese sind alle kampfwertgesteigert worden.

Die **Kampfpioniere** unterteilen sich in eine selbständige Brigade und Pionierkompanien, die direkt den Einsatzbrigaden unterstellt sind. Die Pioniere und die **Infanterie** sind mit einer Reihe von Spezialfahrzeugen wie z.B. 400 Nagmashot/Puma und 200 Achzarit ausgestattet. Primär in den Infanterieeinheiten, aber auch anderen Kampftruppen, finden sich erstaunliche rund 5.500 M113 Mannschaftstransportwagen in zahlreichen Varianten, sowie, eingemottet, immer noch Spezialvarianten der M2/M3 Halbketten amerikanischer Bauart des 2. Weltkrieges *.

Die **Artillerie**, die hauptsächlich aus Panzerhaubitzen M109 besteht, ist in drei aktive Brigaden unterteilt. Mit Stand 2005 befanden sich im Dienst bzw. eingemottet: 140 175 mm M107 Romach, 36 203 mm M110, noch immer 120 155 mm L-33 und insgesamt 600 155 mm M109. Im weiteren sind hier rund 460 gezogene Geschütze sowie etwa 190 Mehrfach-Raketenwerfer (diverser meist sowjetischer Herkunft) einschließlich 48 MLRS zu finden.

Neben diesen Einheiten kämpfen noch eine Anzahl von kleineren, gemischten und unabhängigen mechanisierte Verbänden, die zum Teil von einer undurchsichtigen Vielzahl von **Spezialkräften** (Sayeret) unterstützt werden.

Eine permanente Gliederung und Führung auf Divisionsebene ist bis zum heutigen Tag nicht erwiesen und äußerst unwahrscheinlich. Man spricht aber von je einer Division für die **Militärbezirke** Gaza, Eilat, Golan, Galiläa, Judäa und Samaria.

Das größte taktische Element ist und bleibt die von der Lage abhängig gemischte Brigade. Um die Führung dieser schlagkräftigen Truppe zu

---

* (all figures according to several non-Israeli sources. The Israeli Government has up to the present day not disclosed any figures about IDF strength of personnel or equipment nor of any location of units)

* (Angaben laut verschiedenen nicht-israelischen Quellen. Die israelische Regierung hat bis heute keine offiziellen Angaben über Truppenstärken, Ausrüstungszahlen oder Einheiten veröffentlicht)

To ease command and control functions three **territorial commands**, North, Central and South are in charge. In addition a fourth command, Territorial Defence, can be activated.

How the Israeli Army armoured vehicle complement came into existence and what traditions and experiences are the roots of today's powerful force, will be described in the following chapter with the main aspect on armoured warfare.

A Brief History of Israeli Army Armoured Units

1948 to 1955 – A State and an Army are being made

On the very night the State of Israel was officially founded, 14 May 1948, Arab armies invaded. Egypt, Syria, Lebanon, Jordan, Saudi-Arabia and Iraq sent armed troops towards the new state. The reason for their reaction was a long growing hatred against the Jewish settlers, the unacceptable UN plan to split up the country and the self-declaration of a State of Israel. The Israeli Army, Zahal, was founded on 31 May. Born out of desperation and supported only hesitatingly from abroad it would be capable of stopping the Arab onslaught.

The Zahal, IDF, did not field anything like an armoured corps at that stage. Neither there were any tanks nor capable personnel trained in maintaining these vehicles, driving them and certainly not to go to war in them. In World War 2 the Jewish volunteers with the British Army, for example, were not allowed to join armoured formations. The beginning of the Israeli Armoured Corps began with the "purchase" of two former Syrian Renault R-35 and R-39 tanks that could be captured. In addition a M4 Sherman was "obtained" from a British surplus scrapyard and repaired. Other dubious circumstances saw two British Cromwell tanks, one with a 9-pounder gun and one with a 75mm gun, made available for Zahal. The first true official purchase, however, consisted of ten Hotchkiss H-39 light tanks bought from French Army surplus.

Out of this vehicle complement the first Israeli armoured unit, the 8th Tank Brigade was created. The battle tanks were combined into its 82nd Battalion subdivided into an English Co. (with the Sherman and the two Cromwells) and a Russian Co. (with the ten Hotchkiss H-39). As stated previously the drivers were not local Jews but immigrants from Russia, Great Britain and South Africa. A major drawback of this decision would be the different training of the crews as well as the fact, that they did not speak one common language! A mixture of Russian, English, German, Hebrew and Yiddish would have to do the job.

Other hastily formed armoured formations at that date fielded M3 halftracks and up-armoured trucks with the so-called "Sandwich" armour.

In 1949 further purchases, mostly from foreign scrapyards would allow the creation of larger armoured units. The core of these new units would be M4A1 and M4A2 Sherman tanks (designated in Israel as the M1) in various variants and the newer M4A3E8. In 1955 the first post-WW2 modern tank reached the IDF armoured units, the AMX-13 from France. 100 of these tanks with 75mm guns gave combat capabilities a great boost. Mounting the 75mm main gun of the AMX-13 into 60 Sherman tanks lead to the M50 Super-Sherman of 1955 furthermore improving the IDF arsenal. The core of the Israeli Armoured Corps had now been truly created.

1956 – Crisis at the Suez Canal

In mid-1955 the IDF received another 100 M50 Super-Sherman and more armoured halftracks. In 1956 the crisis between Egypt and Israel escalated and Israel felt the need to occupy the Sinai Peninsula and the Gaza Strip with armoured units on 29 October. British and French elite units also intervened and secured the Suez Canal itself. As a direct reaction to these operations the Soviet Union further expanded military and economical support to Egypt.

erleichtern, wurden drei regionale **Territorialkommandos** aufgestellt: Nord-, Zentral- und Südkommando. Das vierte ist ein Heimatschutz-kommando. Wie sich die israelischen gepanzerten Verbände mit ihrer Fahrzeugvielfalt bis zum heutigen Tag entwickelten, zeigt der folgende kurze Abriss der israelischen Militärgeschichte:

Kurzer Abriss der Geschichte der Gepanzerten Israelischen Verbände

1948 bis 1955 - Ein Staat und eine Armee entsteht

Bereits in der Nacht der israelischen Staatsgründung, am 14. Mai 1948, überfielen die Armeen Ägyptens, Syriens, des Libanons, Transjordaniens, Saudi-Arabiens und des Irak den fast wehrlosen neuen Staat. Grund dafür war der nicht akzeptierte UN-Teilungsplan und die Selbstausrufung des Staates Israels. Bereits am 31. Mai entstand aus dieser Not die israelische Zahal, die später mit zögerlichen Waffenlieferungen und Finanzhilfen aus dem Ausland die Ambitionen der arabischen Staaten zum Stillstand brachte.

Eine israelische Panzertruppe existierte zu Beginn des Krieges nicht. Aber es fehlte nicht nur an Panzern in Israel, sondern auch an fähigem Personal. Jüdische Einheimische hatten kaum Erfahrungen in der Panzertechnik, da es ihnen im 2. Weltkrieg nicht erlaubt war, zum Beispiel in der britischen Panzertruppe zu dienen.

Die Anfänge einer echten „Panzertruppe" in Israel begannen mit der „Beschaffung" von zwei vormals syrischen Renault Panzern R-35 und R-39, die erbeutet werden konnten. Im weiteren wurde ein M4 Sherman auf einem britischen Schrottplatz „besorgt" und wieder fahrbereit gemacht. Durch andere dubiose Umstände gelangte man zusätzlich in den Besitz zweier britischer Cromwell Panzer, einer mit 9-Pfünder Kanone, der andere mit 7,5 cm Kanone. Die erste wirklich professionelle Beschaffungsmaßnahme bestand im Erwerb von zehn Hotchkiss H-39 Panzern aus französischen Beständen.

Aus diesem Fahrzeugbestand konnte die erste israelische Panzereinheit, die 8. Panzerbrigade gebildet werden. Die Kampfpanzer wurden in ihr im 82. Bataillon zusammengefasst, dass in die Englische Kompanie (Sherman und Cromwell Panzer) sowie die Russische Kompanie (Hotchkiss Panzer) untergliedert wurde. Die Panzerfahrer waren, aus bereits vorher beschriebenen Gründen, keine einheimischen Juden, sondern russische, britische und südafrikanische jüdische Immigranten. Diese verfügten weder über eine gemeinschaftliche militärische Ausbildung, noch über die gleiche Kommandosprache. Man sprach Russisch, Englisch, Deutsch, Hebräisch und Jiddisch. Andere hastig aufgestellte gepanzerte Einheiten verfügten zu diesem Zeitpunkt nur über leicht gepanzerte M3 Halbkettenfahrzeuge bzw. zusatzgepanzerte LKW, sogenannte „Sandwich-Panzerwagen", mit unterschiedlicher improvisierter Bewaffnung. Ab 1949 gelang die Beschaffung weiterer Panzerfahrzeuge, zwar wiederum vielfach von ausländischen Schrottplätzen, jedoch nun in einer Anzahl, die es erlaubte, größere Panzerformationen zu bilden. Der Kern dieser neuen Fahrzeugtypen bildeten M4A1 und M4A2 Sherman Panzer (in Israel als M1 bezeichnet) verschiedener Ausführungen, zusätzlich bereits der verbesserte M4A3E8. Im Jahre 1955 gelang schließlich die Beschaffung der ersten modernen Panzerfahrzeuge in Form von 100 AMX-13 aus französischer Fertigung. Der Einbau der 75 mm Kanone des AMX-13 in 60 Sherman Panzer führte zur Variante M50 Super-Sherman des Jahres 1955. Der Anfang der gepanzerten Einheit der IDF war geschaffen.

1956 - Krise um den Suez Kanal

Mitte 1956 erhielt die IDF weitere 100 M50 Super-Sherman und zahlreiche gepanzerte Halbkettenfahrzeuge. Im Laufe des Jahres 1956 verschärfte sich der Konflikt zwischen Ägypten und Israel derart, dass am 29. Oktober israelische Panzertruppen den Gazastreifen und die Sinai-Halbinsel erfolgreich besetzten. Ebenfalls griffen britische und französische Eliteeinheiten in den Konflikt ein und sicherten den Kanal vor dem Zugriff der Konfliktparteien. Als Reaktion unterstützte nun

(Author)

The new AMX-13 allowed the IDF armoured units to effectively counter the Soviet T-34-85 tanks on the battlefield. With the loss of only 30 Israeli tanks 150 tanks and other armoured vehicles plus 350 armoured personnel carriers of the Egyptian Army were destroyed during Operation Kadesh alone.

The years after the Suez War were dominated on the Arab side by a massive arms build-up to cope with the Israeli success in battle. The prime supplier of modern armaments for the Arab nations during this period was the Soviet Union. Among the heavier armoured vehicles was the T-54/55 which should become a major threat to Israel's armoured corps in the years to come.

The Israelis were able to continuously upgrade their equipment to match the increased threat. In addition new tactical concepts were introduced and personnel increased. With the T-54/55 available on the enemy's side a new main battle tank was required. The IDF opted for the British Centurion main battle tank as the best solution in terms of armour. Its weak main gun was soon to be replaced by the much more capable 105mm main gun making the vehicle as capable if not superior to the T-54/55. The Centurion's weaknesses in mobility and mechanical reliability, on the other hand, were soon encountered and forced Israeli designers and mechanics into action. By 1967 most of these drawbacks were eliminated and the core of the IDF tank technology programme had been established.

Another major type of main battle tank to be introduced into IDF inventory was to be the U.S. M48 Patton, purchased between 1960 and 1964. Its appearance in the IDF arsenal at that date was not based on direct U.S. support, the States refused to deliver to Israel directly, but involved the West German Army. From German stocks the first 200 M48s were shipped in secrecy and under U.S. supervision.

Despite the purchase of these new tank types, the IDF armoured forces suffered from a continuous lack of modern armoured vehicles. To cope with the evolving T-54/55 threat more quickly it was decided to mount a new French 105mm gun to existing M1 Sherman turrets. In addition these 200 new vehicles, now designated M51 Isherman (Israeli Sherman), received the modern HVSS running gear and wider tracks.

A further increase on combat effectiveness was secured by fitting 105mm main guns to the M48 and Centurion tanks.

1967 – A War to last Six Days only

The Six-Day-War started after Egypt sent tank formations with the T-54/55 on the Sinai Peninsula and other Arab nations such as Jordan and Syria increased their anti-Israeli policy. This all-around threat was seen in Israel as the prelude of another war. The Gaza Strip was

die UdSSR Ägypten militärisch und wirtschaftlich in viel stärkerem Maße.

Der AMX-13 erlaubte der israelischen Panzertruppe nun den neu an Ägypten gelieferten T-34-85 Panzern sowjetischer Fertigung auf dem Gefechtsfeld effektiv entgegentreten zu können. Bei Verlust von lediglich 30 israelischen Kampfpanzern konnten in den folgenden schweren Gefechten alleine während der Operation Kadesh rund 150 Kampfpanzer und Kampfunterstützungsfahrzeuge sowie rund 350 gepanzerte Mannschaftstransportwagen der ägyptischen Armee ausgeschaltet werden.

Die Jahre nach der Suez Krise von 1956 waren auf arabischer Seite, unter Einbeziehung der bisherigen israelischen Erfolge, von einem massiven Aufbau der gepanzerten Einheiten dominiert. Hauptlieferant modernster Landkriegstechnik sollte bald die Sowjetunion werden, die an fast alle arabischen Staaten neueste Technik wie den in den 1950er Jahren hochmodernen T-54/55 lieferte. Aber auch in Israel selbst hatte man erkannt, dass eine schlagkräftige Panzertruppe der entscheidende Faktor auf den Gefechtsfeldern der Zukunft sein würde. So wurde die Panzertruppe der IDF taktisch neu orientiert und personell stark ausgebaut.

Das Auftauchen des T-54/55 beim Gegner hatte entscheidenden Einfluss auf die anstehenden israelischen Beschaffungsmaßnahmen. Der britische Kampfpanzer Centurion wurde als beste verfügbare Lösung angesehen - seine zu schwache Bordkanone aber bald durch eine 105 mm Variante ersetzt. Diese Bewaffnung sollte sich als äußerst effektiv erweisen, jedoch krankte der Centurion an seiner Unzuverlässigkeit unter Wüstenbedingungen. Israelische Modernisierungsmaßnahmen eliminierten bis 1967 die schlimmsten Probleme - und das Herz israelischer Panzerbaukunst war geschaffen.

Ein weiterer wichtiger Panzertyp, der zwischen 1960 und 1964 beschafft wurde, war der amerikanische M48 Patton. Durch die Weigerung der USA einer direkten Lieferung an Israel, wurden die ersten 200 M48 aus Beständen der Bundeswehr im Geheimen in den Nahen Osten verschifft.

Trotz der Beschaffung dieser neuen Typen herrschte in Israel ein kontinuierlicher Mangel an modernem Panzergerät. Um der Bedrohung durch den T-54/55 schneller gerecht zu werden, wurde daher beschlossen, eine moderne französische 105 mm Kanone in vorhandene M1 Shermans einzubauen. Im weiteren erhielten diese 200 neuen Fahrzeuge M51 Isherman (Israeli Sherman) generell das HVSS Laufwerk und breitere Ketten.

Zusätzlich begann man den M48 durch den Einbau der gleichen 105 mm Kanone wie zuvor beim Centurion zu modernisieren.

Weitere beschaffte Centurion erhielten ebenfalls diese Kampfwertsteigerung.

at that date Egyptian territory and the West-Bank belonged to Jordan. The Israeli solution for the worsening situation was quickly found - A pre-emptive strike! On 05 June 1967 the Israeli air force hit the Egyptian forces hard. Land forces cut them off from their homeland. The Egyptian Army was swiftly facing a bitter defeat. Out of 935 Egyptian tanks employed, more than 820 were lost, among them 373 of the feared T-54/55 tanks! The Egyptian soldiers fled in panic and on 08 June IDF armoured forces had already crossed the peninsula.

On the Jordanian frontline Israeli armoured units equipped with the ageing M51 Isherman successfully beat off Jordanian M47 and M48 tanks. The clashes with Syria were mostly infantry battles.

On 11 June the ceasefire was signed with the Sinai-Peninsula, the Gaza-Strip, the West-Bank, the historical part of Jerusalem and the Golan-Heights falling into Israeli hands.

Among the war booty for the IDF were nearly 100 out of 170 Jordanian M48 and M48A1 tanks, which were quickly absorbed. In general the Israeli Armoured Corps had established itself as a fast and highly flexible military formation with an outstanding esprit-de-corps and will to fight. Egypt had been much better equipped, fielding the T-54/55 with its 100mm gun and the super-heavy IS III but IDF tactics and training prevailed. A myth was born.

Many of the captured Arab T-54/55 tanks could be repaired, rearmed with 105mm guns and introduced into IDF inventory under the designation Tiran 4 and Tiran 5. The Centurion and M48 tanks had shown their combat effectiveness but now all received the 105mm guns and the engine was technically further improved.

Along these improvements the search for a possible successor for the Centurion and M48 was already at hand. The best solution was identified as the purchase and eventual co-production of the British Chieftain. As this proved impossible for political reasons, the U.S. M60A1 main battle tank with 105mm gun was chosen. The new vehicle reached the IDF from 1970 along with other U.S. equipment such as the M107 and M109 self-propelled guns.

On the Arab side the chance for future victory was once more seen in a massive arms build-up. The Soviet Union supplied quantities not only to replace the losses but to increase the number of armoured vehicles in general. Among the new types of armoured vehicles delivered was the T-62 main battle tank with 115mm main gun. Of much greater importance for the future development of Israel's Armoured Corps, however, was to be a tiny little guided anti-tank missile: The "Malyutka", or in NATO terms: AT-3 Sagger.

1973 Yom-Kippur – The October War

On 06 October 1973 Egyptian and Syrian Forces again attacked Israel. Because of the Yom-Kippur holidays the IDF's state of alert was neglected and they were completely surprised. Syrian forces began to advance with 1,400 armoured vehicles in the Golan Heights and Egyptian tank formations crushed Israeli defences on the Suez Canal.

1967 - Ein Krieg der nur sechs Tage dauerte

Der Sechstage-Krieg entbrannte zwischen Israel, Ägypten, Jordanien und Syrien, nachdem ägyptische Panzerverbände mit T-54/55 Kampfpanzern auf die Sinai-Halbinsel verlegten und die weitere arabische Expansion auch anderer arabischer Staaten in Israel als kurz bevorstehende reale Bedrohung erkannt wurde. Der Gaza-Streifen war zu dem Zeitpunkt ägyptisch kontrolliert und die West-Bank gehörte zu Jordanien.

Der Krieg begann am 05. Juni 1967 mit einem israelischen Präventivschlag aus der Luft. Bereits kurz darauf waren die ägyptischen Truppen vom Heimatland abgeschnitten und standen am Rande einer bitteren Niederlage. Von 935 eingesetzten Panzern verlor Ägypten mehr als 820, darunter 373 der so gefürchteten T-54/55. Die Ägypter gerieten in Panik und am 08. Juni standen bereits israelische Panzerspitzen wieder am Suez-Kanal. An der Jordanien Front konnten sich z.B. israelische M51 Isherman Einheiten erfolgreich mit jordanischen M47 und M48 messen. Die Auseinandersetzungen mit Syrien fanden fast ohne Panzerbeteiligung statt. Am 11. Juni wurde der Waffenstillstand unterzeichnet und Israel hatte die Sinai-Halbinsel, den Gaza-Streifen, die West-Bank, die historische Altstadt von Jerusalem und die Golan-Höhen dem Gegner entreißen können.

Neben den bereits im Dienst befindlichen M48 Kampfpanzern konnte Israel in diesem Krieg fast 100 von 170 jordanischen M48 und M48A1 erbeuten. Die israelische Panzertruppe definierte sich als schneller und flexibler Kampfverband, der durch Improvisation und Kampfgeist erfolgreich war. Ägypten war zwar mit seinen T-54/55 mit der 100 mm Kanone und sogar schweren Josef Stalin 3 besser bewaffnet, aber in Taktik und Kampfgeist den Israelis absolut unterlegen. Ein Mythos war geboren.

Bei den arabischen erbeuteten T-54/55 Panzern wurden teilweise die 100 mm Kanonen gegen solche mit 105 mm ausgetauscht, die Panzer in Tiran 4 und Tiran 5 umbenannt und in die israelische Panzertruppe integriert. Die Centurion und M48 hatten ihren Kampfwert bewiesen, wurden jedoch nun alle auf den Bewaffnungsstand 105 mm geführt und besonders im Motorenbereich verbessert.

Gleichzeitig begann auch die Suche nach einem moderneren Nachfolger für M48 und Centurion. Die israelische Armee bevorzugte die besser gepanzerten britischen Modelle und hatte bereits 1967 den Chieftain in Erprobung. Aus politischen Erwägungen heraus kam es jedoch nicht zu dessen Beschaffung. Stattdessen wurde der amerikanische M60A1 Patton mit 105 mm Kanone ab 1970 eingeführt. Im gleichen Zeitraum erwarb man ebenfalls die amerikanischen Selbstfahrlafetten M107 und M109.

Der arabische Gegner erwarb mittlerweile massiv weiteres sowjetisches Kriegsgerät, um die Verluste auszugleichen sowie die Kampfstärke generell zu erhöhen. Bei den Kampfpanzern sei hier der T-62 mit 115 mm Bordkanone zu nennen. Viel wichtiger und entscheidender im nächsten Konflikt würde jedoch eine kleine ferngelenkte Panzerabwehrrakete sein, die mehr Einfluss auf die mechanisierte Kriegs-

The Egyptian operation on the Suez Peninsula, including crossing the Suez Canal, can only be described as one of the masterpieces of modern land warfare. Covered by a nearly impenetrable screen of surface-to-air missiles the Egyptian land forces crossed the canal and broke through the weak Israeli resistance. The quickly alerted Israeli armoured units rushed to the frontline only to run into a trap of Egyptian Sagger-armed highly mobile anti-tank teams. IDF losses were appalling. Only desperate measures and sheer luck, as the Egyptian forces left the security of the missile-screen - a foolish mistake, allowed the IDF to crush the Egyptian advance and push forward to the Canal once more, to cross it on 16 October.

The battles on the Syrian front were dominated by heavy clashes at short distances. Only after bitter fighting and severe losses the IDF finally prevailed and pushed forward, finally nearly reaching Damascus! The war on all frontlines officially came to an end on 22 October 1973.

The Yom-Kippur War, or October War, showed the vulnerability of tank units in action without close infantry support as well as the high efficiency of the new anti-tank missiles. These two facts became a crucial factor in the decision making of the IDF to the present day and led to armoured infantry/engineer carriers such as the Achzarit and the Puma, advanced armour protection such as Blazer reactive armour for the main battle tanks and ultimately to the introduction of Israel's very own tank design, the Merkava.

In 1973 Syria and Egypt primarily used the T-54/55 as well as the new T-62 with the 115mm main gun. Captured T-62 were later to be reused within the IDF under the designation Tiran 6. The IDF Armoured Corps at that date was mainly equipped with the ageing M51 Isherman, the M48, M60 and Centurion all armed with the 105mm main gun. To compensate for the heavy losses the U.S.A. started delivering more M48, M60 and M60A1 to Israel shortly after the war. More M48A5 and M60A3 followed in the years to come. The M60 Magach now became the backbone of the IDF armoured units. However, the M60's vulnerability to anti-tank missile fire and its tendency to catch fire easily led to constant improvements of the Magachs up to the Magach 6 Batash with hybrid add-on armour elements and finally the Magach 7C. Another critical factor was encountered in the lack of capable night-fighting equipment for the IDF tanks, while the Arab/Soviet tanks were equipped with such devices from the production line. Measures to close this gap in technology also followed.

1978 – Operation Litani – Trouble in Lebanon

After several attacks by the Palestinian Liberation Organisation PLO from Lebanon into Israel, the Zahal sent a 15,000 strong expeditionary force into southern Lebanon. The cross-frontier operation gave the Israeli Armoured Corps a taste of things to come in the next years – the massive and costly employment of armoured units in combat in urban area fighting against guerrillas.

1982 – Peace For Galilee – Back to Lebanon

On 06 June 1982 the IDF launched their attack into Lebanon to finally destroy the PLO. Approx. 10,000 PLO irregular fighters were soon trapped inside Beirut's city perimeters. What followed involved harsh urban warfare and house-to-house fighting using infantry units, Sayeret special forces and armoured vehicles. The PLO finally had to give in and left Beirut, Israel stayed in central Lebanon until 1985 and left the southern security perimeter only in 2000.

Combat in Lebanon involved numerous Israeli vehicle types: The armoured personnel carrier M113, designated Zelda, and its subvariants, the Centurion Nagmashot armoured infantry carrier with Blazer reactive armour, M60A1 Magach 6 main battle tanks also with reactive armour as the Centurion Shot main battle tanks. M109A1 self propelled howitzers were committed to the fight as were the first, brand new Is-

führung und die Ausrüstung besonders der israelischen Armee haben sollte als alles andere seit der Gründung des Staates: Die „Maljutka", oder im NATO-Jargon: AT-3 Sagger!

1973 - Yom Kippur - Krieg am Versöhnungsfest

Am 06. Oktober 1973 überfielen erneut Ägypten und Syrien Israel. Da während des jüdischen Versöhnungsfestes kaum Verteidigungsmaßnahmen getroffen wurden, ist die Zahal gänzlich überrascht worden. Syrische Truppen rückten mit fast 1.400 gepanzerten Fahrzeugen auf die Golan-Höhen vor und ägyptische Panzerspitzen durchbrachen die israelischen Stellungen am Suez-Kanal.

Die ägyptischen Streitkräfte wurden glänzend geführt und konnten neue Taktiken erfolgreich gegen die IDF einsetzen. So garantierte ein enger Schirm von Boden-Luft Raketen die Luftüberlegenheit auf dem Gefechtsfeld, und mobil eingesetzte Sagger-Teams fügten der zur Front eilenden israelischen Panzertruppe schwerste Verluste zu. Nur mit dem Mut der Verzweiflung gelang es den israelischen Truppen den Gegner zu zerschlagen und ebenfalls vorzudringen, dies aber erst, als die ägyptischen Streitkräfte ihren Fla-Rak Schirm nach einer krassen Fehlentscheidung hinter sich ließen.

Im Kampf gegen die syrische Armee an den Golan Höhen kam es zu schwersten Gefechten auf oft kürzeste Distanzen. Erst nach schwerem Ringen und schmerzlichen Verlusten konnte der Gegner überwunden werden. Nach Ergreifung der Initiative stand die IDF aber schon kurz darauf wenige Kilometer vor Damaskus.

Am 16. Oktober setzte die Zahal an der ägyptischen Front über den Suez-Kanal und zwang so die ägyptischen Streitkräfte zur Aufgabe. Am 22. Oktober herrschte bereits wieder Waffenruhe.

Der Yom-Kippur Krieg von 1973 zeigt vor allem die Verwundbarkeit von gepanzerten Einheiten ohne begleitende Infanterieeinheiten, und die Schwächen der Kampfpanzer gegenüber Panzerabwehrlenkflugkörpern. Diese beiden Tatsachen sollten in den folgenden Jahren zu einem gründlichen Umdenken innerhalb der IDF führen, und schließlich in gepanzerten Begleitfahrzeugen wie dem Achzarit oder Puma, in erheblich verbesserter Panzertechnik in Form von Reaktivpanzerung (Blazer) sowie ultimativ zur Einführung des ersten eigenen israelischen Kampfpanzers, des Merkava, führen.

Syrien und Ägypten setzten 1973 neben dem T-54/55 den Kampfpanzer T-62 mit 115 mm Kanone ein. Erbeutete T-62 sollten innerhalb der IDF später als Tiran 6 eingesetzt werden. Israel stand zu diesem Zeitpunkt neben dem M51 Isherman und Centurion der M48 nachgerüstet mit der 105 mm Kanone und der M60A1, ebenfalls mit einer 105 mm Kanone bewaffnet, zur Verfügung. Um die schweren Verluste an diesen Typen auszugleichen, lieferten die USA nach den Kämpfen eine Anzahl von M48, M60 und M60A1 Kampfpanzern an die stark dezimierte israelische Panzertruppe. Es folgten später weitere Kampfpanzer M48A5 und M60A3. Der M60 Magach wurde nun zum Rückgrat der israelischen Panzertruppe. Die Lehren aus den Kämpfen waren aber, dass der Magach schnell in Brand geriet und den neuen Panzerabwehrwaffen wie der Sagger kaum standhalten konnte. Diese Erkenntnisse führten zu einer permanenten Weiterentwicklung des Magach, bis zur Magach 6 Batash Variante mit hybriden Zusatzpanzerungselementen und schließlich dem Magach 7C. Eine wesentliche Lehre aus den Konfrontationen mit den arabischen konventionellen Truppen lag auch darin, dass die dort genutzten sowjetischen Panzermodelle bereits standardmäßig über Infrarot-Nachtsichtgeräte verfügten. Erst nach dem Krieg konnte die Zahal moderne Restlichtverstärkergeräte für ihre Panzer beschaffen und diese technologische Lücke schließen.

1978 - Operation „Litani" - Aufräumen im Libanon

Nach mehreren Angriffen der PLO Untergrundorganisation auf Israel aus dem Libanon, entsandte die Zahal eine 15.000 Mann starke Expeditionstruppe in den Süden des Landes. Diese Grenzoperation war jedoch ein Vorgeschmack auf das, was die israelischen gepanzerten Truppen bis zu heutigen Tage im Libanon erwarten würde: Der mas-

raeli produced Merkava 1 main battle tanks. The Arab forces, Lebanon and Syria fielded the T-34-85, the T-54/55, T-62 and AMX-13. All of which were outclassed by IDF armour at that date.

Based on unconfirmed reports, however, the IDF lost no less than 300 of their 1,025 employed armoured vehicles, many of them to man-portable rocket-propelled grenades and anti-tank missiles. Of these vehicles 108 were heavily damaged, 92 put out of action (52 of which totally destroyed). Among these were 37 M60 Magach, eight Centurion Shot and seven Merkava 1. The Arab side lost, according to unconfirmed reports, 500 main battle tanks. Additional 200 seem to have been captured by the IDF. The PLO had to leave all their heavy equipment behind when being evacuated to Tunisia.

One of the lessons learned from this conflict was the need to compensate for the guerrilla tactics and the anti-tank effectiveness of shoulder-launched anti-tank weapons especially in urban area warfare. The bitter lesson of seeing so many M113s being lost, saw the introduction of better armoured and more survivable armoured fighting vehicles.

1992 – Back to Lebanon

The spring of 1989 had seen the Barak Brigade receive their first Merkava 3 main battle tank. With its new 120mm main gun it was now superior to all other main battle tanks in the region.

In 1992 the IDF launched a number of limited military operations against the anti-Israeli Hezbollah militia in southern Lebanon. The vehicles used for these actions included the M113 now with TOGA stand-off armour and the improved Merkava 2 and Merkava 3 main battle tanks. In addition the new Achzarit armoured infantry carrier, converted from surplus T-54/55 hulls, and the Puma armoured engineer vehicle, based on surplus Centurion hulls, were used. The Centurion Nagmashot had previously also been improved, uparmoured and redesignated first as the Nagmachon or as the latest Centurion conversion the Nakpadon. These were used as direct support vehicles for security operations.

2002 – The Battle for Jenin

In April 2002 Zahal carried out a major anti-terror operation on the West Bank. One of the targets of the operation "Defensive Shield" was to seize the Palestinian refugee camps to destroy terrorist cells operation from there.

A disastrous ambush, carried out during the first phase of the operation, however, led to a change of tactics with the IDF forces. The armoured D9 dozers of the engineers were now directly employed as spearheads in the operation. The reason for this unusual practice was the fact that many buildings were mined so heavily that clearing them would have taken weeks. The simple and more effective solution was to tear down the buildings completely. In addition the dozers were effective in clearing mined roadblocks as well.

(IDF Spokesman)

sive und schwierige Einsatz von Panzern in bebautem Gelände gegen eine Stadtguerilla.

1982 - Operation „Frieden für Galiläa" - Einsatz im Libanon

Am 06. Juni 1982 begann die IDF mit dem Angriff auf den Libanon um endgültig die PLO zu zerschlagen. Circa 10.000 palästinensische Kämpfer wurden in Beirut eingeschlossen. In schweren Häuserkämpfen mit Infanterie, Sayeret-Spezialeinheiten und Kampfpanzern konnten diese zum Abzug gezwungen werden. Israel blieb bis 1985 im Zentrum Libanons und zog erst im Jahr 2000 vorübergehend aus der südlichen Pufferzone ab.

In den Kämpfen kamen einen Vielzahl von gepanzerten israelischen Fahrzeugen zum Einsatz: der gepanzerte Mannschaftstransportwagen M113, genannt Zelda, und zahlreiche Abarten dieses Fahrzeugs, Centurion Nagmashot Schützenpanzer mit Blazer-Reaktivpanzerung, Kampfpanzer M60A1 Magach 6 ebenfalls mit Blazer-Rüstsätzen wie die Kampfpanzer Centurion Shot, Panzerhaubitzen M109AL und natürlich die ersten Exemplare des brandneuen Kampfpanzers Merkava 1 aus israelischer Eigenproduktion.

Der arabische Gegner, Libanon und Syrien zog unter anderem mit den Kampfpanzern T-34-85, T-54/55, T-62 und AMX-13 ins ungleiche Gefecht.

Laut unbestätigten Frontberichten verlor die IDF trotzdem circa 300 von ihren 1.025 eingesetzten Fahrzeugen, viele davon an Teams mit Panzerfäusten und Panzerabwehrlenkflugkörpern. Von den Fahrzeugen wurden 108 schwer beschädigt, 92 durch direkte Treffer abgeschossen, von denen wiederum 52 total zerstört wurden. Dazu zählten auch 37 M60 Magach, acht Centurion Shot und sieben Merkava. Im Gegenzug verloren die arabischen Truppen angeblich bis zu 500 Kampfpanzer, weitere 200 wurden durch die IDF erbeutet. Die PLO ließ ihr ganzes schweres Gerät zurück, bevor sie ins Exil nach Tunesien ging.

Aus den Lehren des Konfliktes entstanden eine Vielzahl von neuen IDF Fahrzeugvarianten, um mit dem Einfallsreichtum der Untergrundkämpfer und der fortgeschrittenen Panzerabwehrtechnik auch in stark bebautem Gelände Schritt zu halten. Besonders aus diesen Lehren verbesserte man in den nächsten Jahren die Dachpanzerung der Fahrzeuge. Die mit M113 ausgerüsteten Einheiten bezahlten bitteres Lehrgeld aufgrund ungenügender Panzerung dieser Mannschaftstransportwagen.

1992 - Wieder zurück im Libanon

Im Frühjahr 1989 hatte bereits die Barak Brigade die ersten Merkava 3 bekommen. Mit der größeren 120 mm Kanone war der neue Merkava allen arabischen Gegnern nun haushoch überlegen.

Im Jahre 1992 startete die IDF gegen die anti-israelischen Hisbollah-Milizen im Südlibanon einige begrenzte Militäroperationen. Dabei kamen bereits die bekannten M113 mit der neuen TOGA-Panzerung zum Einsatz, ebenso wie die verbesserten Kampfpanzer Merkava 2 und 3. Zusätzlich hatte man T-54/55 Fahrzeugwannen zu schweren Achzarit Sturmpanzern und Centurion Fahrzeugwannen zu Puma Pionierpanzern umgebaut. Der Centurion Nagmashot wurde erheblich gegen Angriffe verbessert und so entstanden die Nagmachon und Nakpadon Varianten. Die beiden letzteren wurden direkt als Unterstützungsfahrzeuge für Sicherheitsoperationen umgebaut.

2002 - Die Schlacht um Jenin

Im April 2002 führte die Zahal eine groß angelegte Anti-Terroroperation in der West-Bank durch. Als Teilziel der Operation „Schutzschild" wurde das palästinensische Flüchtlingslager Jenin von israelischen Truppen besetzt, um die dortige Untergrundorganisation zu zerschlagen.

Nach einem fatalen Hinterhalt in den ersten Tagen der Operation hatte sich allerdings die Taktik der IDF stark verändert. Die gepanzerten D9 Planierraupen wurden jetzt nicht mehr nur zur Pionierunterstützung herangezogen, sondern nahmen als Spitzenfahrzeuge am Einsatz teil.

(IDF Spokesman)

The tactics of the Intifada fighters initially was to lure the IDF soldiers into the narrow city roads, separating them from their armoured vehicle support, to engage them in close-quarter combat with incendiary devices. After days of fighting the battlefield had been reduced to a rectangular zone of 400x200 metres where the dozers had flattened the area completely. The same experiences were made in the Gaza Strip.

2002 – The Siege of Ramallah

After a devastating Palestinian suicide bombing in Tel Aviv armoured units of the IDF advanced on 20 September to seize the official residence of the President of Palestine Yasser Arafat in Ramallah to arrest and isolate him. Israeli assault engineers, supported by armoured vehicles, destroyed numerous Palestinian official buildings as well as weapons storage and missile production facilities. Merkava main battle tanks fired their rounds into buildings to clear safe passage for the Special Forces. In addition IDF snipers and the bodyguard of President Arafat exchanged fire. The D9 dozers once more were responsible for removing burning car wrecks and to tear down buildings.
After nine days President Arafat's official residence had been flattened to the ground – once more a proof of the efficiency of the mixed Israeli battle group fighting from company to battalion size in specialised missions in urban warfare. In addition almost all operations were carried out under armour support. Of special value here were the armoured engineer and infantry vehicles such as the Achzarit and the Puma.

2004 – Back in Gaza – Operation "Rainbow"

To finally seal off the smuggling of small arms through tunnels and thus the continued attacks on Israel in 2004 the IDF carried out a mission to destroy buildings in the Gaza Strip. The operation ended on 21 May after combat-experienced mechanised units incorporating large formations of main battle tanks and armoured personnel carriers had been employed with great success. The spearhead once more were the proven dozers, saving the infantry a lot of time by simply tearing down the buildings in question. These tactics have proved effective. They help prevent casualties amongst the infantry from improvised explosive devices. The tactics save time and if a dozer should be lost it is cheaper to replace than a Merkava.

2004 – Operation "Day of Atonement"

After Israel had once more been the target for missile attacks from the Gaza Strip the IDF invaded on 29 September 2004 with a powerful task force. The target was to create a ten kilometre wide demilitarised zone to make future attacks impossible. According to media reports 2,000 soldiers and 200 armoured vehicles were in action on the Israeli side. As before heavy street-fighting between Hamas militia and Israeli mechanised units took place. Despite the established threat offered by RPG-7 rocket propelled grenades and incendiary devices the IDF units advanced under the protection of their armoured vehicles. In case of

Die handelsüblichen Dozer wurden von diesem Zeitpunkt an verstärkt mit Zusatzpanzerungen versehen. Grund dafür war unter anderem auch die hohe Anzahl von verminten Häusern und hunderte von großen Sprengfallen am Straßenrand.
Taktik der Intifada Kämpfer war es ursprünglich gewesen, die schweren israelischen mechanisierten Verbände immer tiefer in die verwinkelten Gassen von Jenin hineinzulocken und mit Sprengmitteln zu attackieren. Das Zentrum der Kämpfe war zum Schluss nur ein Rechteck von circa 400 mal 200 Metern und sie endeten damit, dass die D9 Dozer das Gelände dem Erdboden gleichmachten. Auch in Gaza machte man gleichartige bittere Erfahrungen.

2002 - Belagerung in Ramallah

Nach einem verheerenden palästinensischen Selbstmordanschlag in Tel Aviv rückten gepanzerte IDF Verbände am 20. September in den Amtssitz von Palästinenserpräsident Jassir Arafat in Ramallah ein, um ihn festzusetzen und zu isolieren. Israelische Sturmpioniere sprengten unter dem Schutz von gepanzerten Fahrzeugen eine Vielzahl von palästinensischen Regierungsgebäuden. Merkava Kampfpanzer schossen Breschen in Häuser und Mauern, um das Vordringen von Sondereinheiten zu gewährleisten. Ebenso lieferten sich Zahal Scharfschützen und die Leibwache von Arafat Heckenschützengefechte. Nebenbei zerstörten andere Truppen palästinensische Raketen- und Waffenwerkstätten. Die imposanten D9 Dozer räumten wiederum brennende Autowracks beiseite und brachten Gebäude zum Einsturz.
Nach neun Tagen Belagerung war der Amtssitz von Arafat fast vollständig zerstört. Hier bewies sich wieder einmal die dynamische Schlagkraft israelischer gemischter Verbände, die in Kompanie- bis Bataillonsstärke komplexe Sondereinsätze in bebautem Gebiet durchführen konnten. Zudem fanden fast alle Teiloperationen unter Panzerschutz statt. Als besonders effektiv erwiesen sich auch die gepanzerten Infanterie- und Pionierfahrzeuge wie der Achzarit und der Puma.

2004 - Zurück in Gaza - Operation „Regenbogen"

Um den Waffenschmuggel durch Tunnel zu beenden und die permanenten Angriffe auf Israel zu unterbinden, führte die IDF in Gaza im Jahre 2004 eine regelrechte „Abriss"-Aktion durch, die am 21. Mai endete. Zum Einsatz kamen wieder die bewährten mechanisierten Verbände mit einem großen Anteil an Kampfpanzern und schweren gepanzerten Mannschaftstransportwagen. Speerspitze waren ebenso die bereits bekannten D9 Dozer, die den Soldaten den Weg bahnten. Anstatt Gebäude zu stürmen und zu durchsuchen, wurden sie einfach abgerissen, da sie meistens vermint waren. Diese Taktik kann man mittlerweile als etabliert bezeichnen, da sie erfolgreich und effizient ist. Ebenso schont sie das Leben israelischer Soldaten die sonst den vielen Sprengfallen kaum gewachsen wären. Tatsächlich bleibt vor Ort kaum die Zeit, um diese fachgerecht zu räumen. Auch würde kaum ein IDF Kommandeur dafür seine wertvollen EOD-Kampfmittelräumtrupps riskieren, die eher im Kernland zum Zivilschutz und zur Inneren Sicherheit benötigt werden. Ebenso möchte man keinen teuren Merkava Kampfpanzer aufs Spiel setzen.

2004 - Operation „Tag der Buße"

Nachdem Israel wiederholt aus dem Gaza-Streifen mit Raketen beschossen wurde, marschierte die IDF am 29. September mit einem starken Einsatzverband ein. Ziel war es, eine zehn Kilometer breite Pufferzone zu errichten, um die Raketenangriffe auf Israel zu unterbinden. Laut Medienberichten kamen bis zu 2.000 Soldaten und 200 Panzerfahrzeuge zum Einsatz. Wie schon zuvor kam es wiederholt zu erbitterten Straßenkämpfen zwischen den Hamas-Milizionären und den mechanisierten israelischen Einheiten. Unter der Deckung von Kampfpanzern und schwer geschützten Truppentransportern rückten diese jedoch kontinuierlich vor. Improvisierte Sprengladungen und RPG-7 Panzerabwehrgeschosse waren dabei eine klassische Bedrohung für die Soldaten. Zu diesem Zeitpunkt konnten die verwundbaren

the M113 only the newer types fitted with TOGA stand-off armour were now considered feasible for that type of combat. The "kings of the asymmetric battlefield" were once more the Merkava main battle tanks, the Centurion-based armoured infantry carriers and the ubiquitous D9 dozers.

2006 – Escalation after Kidnapping – War in Lebanon and Gaza

In July 2006 Israeli soldiers have been kidnapped in Gaza and at the Lebanese border. The IDF was adamant about returning the soldiers home to their families and to neutralise the kidnappers. The following operation was called "Deserved Payment" to be later changed into Operation "Change of Direction".

As a result of the following Israeli military action Hamas irregulars from Gaza launched short-range rockets and Hezbollah fighters from southern Lebanon fired long-range missiles into Israel. The IDF reacted by bombing targets in Lebanon from the air. After only ten days the Israeli Air Force already had flown 3,000 sorties. Just a few days later the whole situation escalated in such a manner that thousands of Lebanese citizens started fleeing from their homes. Lebanon was on the brink of a full scale war. Israeli ground troops now crossed the border into Lebanon. Spearheading every IDF column were the combat experienced heavy mechanised units under aerial cover from attack helicopters und unmanned aerial vehicles. IDF self-propelled howitzers fired on Hamas strongpoints in Gaza and Hezbollah strongpoints in southern Lebanon.

It took more than a month of heavy combat until a ceasefire could be signed in mid-August 2006. The last Israeli soldier left Lebanese soil on 01 October 2006.

The future of Israeli Armoured Vehicles

The Israeli Army, IDF, had to face a numerical superior enemy more than once in the wars it fought since 1948. It was more than effective soldiering and good leadership that helped provide victory against the odds. The IDF has always focused on rapidly adapting equipment to match their tactical doctrine and operational environment. Inside the IDF Armoured Corps this approach always guaranteed a highly flexible reaction to swiftly changing battlefield scenarios, ranging from self defence with improvised armour in 1948 via the large formation tank battles in the desert of 1973 to today's asymmetrical warfare in urban areas in 2006. All the experiences of the past can be found in today' s tactics and technology, making the modern IDF Armoured Corps an unbeatable opponent on its own territory.

Questions about the future technical development of IDF vehicles and the tactics they might adopt are as yet unclear. However, with all possible future scenarios in mind, one thing can be said for sure – the IDF armoured units will be ready for it!

Soeren Suenkler & Jochen Vollert, October 2006

(IDF Spokesman)

Standard-Mannschaftstransportwagen M113 und deren Abarten dem Waffenarsenal der Hamas und der libanesischen Hisbollah schon lange nicht mehr standhalten. Nur aufgerüstete Fahrzeuge mit der Zusatzpanzerung TOGA kamen für einen Einsatz an der Front noch in Frage. Die meisten Standard-M113 leisten nur noch Dienst im rückwärtigen Raum zur Kampfunterstützung. König der asymmetrischen Schlacht bleibt der Kampfpanzer Merkava sowie die umfassend umgebauten Panzerfahrzeuge auf Centurion Fahrgestellen und natürlich die D9 Planierraupen.

2006 - Eskalation um eine Geiselnahme
Krieg im Libanon und in Gaza

Nachdem im Juli 2006 kurz hintereinander israelische Soldaten bei Gaza und an der libanesischen Grenze überfallen und entführt wurden, setzte die Zahal alles daran, diese zu finden und die Entführer zu neutralisieren. Israel nannte die Operation „Gerechter Lohn", die später in Operation „Richtungsänderung" umbenannt wurde.

Als Antwort auf die folgenden Militäraktionen im Gaza-Streifen beschossen die Hamas aus Gaza und die Hisbollah-Milizen aus dem Südlibanon Israel mit weitreichenden Raketen. Im Gegenzug bombardierte die israelische Luftwaffe Ziele im gegnerischen Gebiet. Nach zehn Tagen hatte sie schon über 3.000 Einsätze geflogen. Bereits wenige Tage später eskalierte die Lage dermaßen, dass Tausende Flüchtlinge den Libanon überstürzt verließen und die Region am Rande eines konventionellen Krieges stand. Israelische Truppen rückten nun in den Libanon vor. Speerspitze eines jeden israelischen Stoßtrupps waren, wie gewohnt, schwere mechanisierte Verbände unter der Deckung von Kampfhubschraubern und unbemannten Drohnen. Zusätzlich beschossen israelische Panzerhaubitzen Hamas Stützpunkte im Gaza-Streifen und die der Hisbollah im Südlibanon.

Erst nach einem Monat schwerer Gefechte kam es zu einem vorläufigen Waffenstillstand Mitte August 2006. Zweieinhalb Monate nach Beginn des Krieges verließ der letzte israelische Soldat den Libanon am 01. Oktober 2006.

Die Zukunft der israelischen gepanzerten Fahrzeuge

Die israelische Armee, IDF, stand in zahlreichen Kriegen seit 1948 immer wieder einem zahlenmäßig stark überlegenen Gegner gegenüber. Nicht nur einmal waren es nur dem Geschick der Soldaten und der militärischen Führung zu verdanken, dass man um Haaresbreite der totalen Vernichtung entgehen konnte. Entgegen den Traditionen anderer, westlicher wie auch östlicher Streitkräfte, setzt man innerhalb der IDF jedoch auf die schnelle Reaktion auf aufgetretene Probleme. Wird ein taktischer Fehler oder eine technische Unzulänglichkeit erkannt, dauert es nur vergleichsweise kurze Zeit, bis effektive Resultate und Verbesserungen der Truppe zu einer noch effektiveren Gefechtsführung an die Hand gegeben werden können.

Innerhalb der gepanzerten Truppen, und speziell natürlich der Panzertruppe, konnte man sich so immer schnell auf neue und oft unerwartete Gegebenheiten in einem vielfältigen Gefechtszenario - von der schieren Selbstverteidigung bewaffnet nur mit improvisiertem Fahrzeuggerät 1948, über die große Panzerschlacht gegen eine gut ausgestattete Armee in der offenen Wüste 1973 bis hin zum Kampf gegen irreguläre Kombatanten in bebauten Gebieten im Libanon 2006 - reagieren. Die gegenwärtige Ausrüstung mit Fahrzeuggerät ist solchermaßen hochspezialisiert, dass der modernen israelischen Armee auf eigenem Boden kein Gegner siegreich gegenübertreten könnte.

Die Frage, wohin sich die Fahrzeugtechnik und der taktische Einsatz von gepanzerten Formationen in den nächsten Jahren und Jahrzehnten im Falle Israels entwickeln könnte, ist aufgrund der Vielfalt der möglichen Szenarien nicht abschließend zu beantworten. Eines ist jedoch sicher: Die moderne israelische Armee wird in jedem Falle eine Lösung für jedes anstehende Problem finden.

Soeren Suenkler & Jochen Vollert, Oktober 2006

(Author)

Selected Bibliography / *Ausgewählte Literaturhinweise*

Title / *Titel*	Author/*Autor*	Publisher/*Verlag*	Year/*Jahr*
° **Merkava - A History of Israel's Main Battle Tank**	Gelbart	Tankograd	2005
° Vanguard 19 - **Armour of the Middle East Wars 1948-78**	Zaloga	Osprey	1981
° New Vanguard 21 - **Merkava MBT 1977-1996**	Katz/Sarson	Osprey	1997
° New Vanguard 93 - **Modern Israeli Tanks and Infantry Carriers 1985-2004**	Gelbart	Osprey	2004
° Concord 1001 - **Israel's Armor Might**	Katz	Concord	1989
° **Israeli War Machine**	Hogg	Quarto	1983
° **Israel's Armor on Action**	Eshel	Eshel Dramit	1978
° Tanks Illustrated 24 - **Modern Israeli Tanks**	Katz	Arms&Armour Press	1987
° Tanks Illustrated 03 - **Israeli Tanks**	Zaloga	Arms&Armour Press	1983
° **Israeli Tank Battles - Yom Kippur to Lebanon**	Katz	Arms&Armour Press	1988
° **Chariots of the Desert**	Eshel	Brassey´s	1989
° War Data 10 - **Israel's New Merkava**	Eshel	Eshel Dramit	1981
° War Data 17 - **Merkava 2**	Eshel	Eshel Dramit	1984
° Military Briefs 2 - **Israeli Tank Based Carriers**	Gelbart	Mouse House	2000
° **Shield of Zion - Israeli Defence Forces**	Lorch/Lorch	Howell	1991
° **The Israeli Army**	Eshel	Eshel Dramit	1978
° Men-at-Arms 127 - **Israeli Army in the Middle East Wars**	Laffin/Chappell	Osprey	1982
° Elite 08 - **Israeli Defence Forces since 1973**	Katz/Volstad	Osprey	1990
° Elite 18 - **Israeli Elite Units since 1948**	Katz/Volstad	Osprey	1988
° **Israel' Army**	Katz	Presidio	1990
° Concord 7009 - **Tank Battles of the Mid-East Wars**	Zaloga	Concord	1998
° **The Yom Kippur War**	Eshel	Eshel Dramit	1978
° Defence Update 42 - **10 Years Yom Kippur War**	Eshel	Eshel Dramit	1983
° **The Six Day War**	Eshel	Eshel Dramit	1979
° Concord 1003 - **Battleground Lebanon**	Katz/Volstad	Concord	1990
° **The Lebanon War 1982**	Eshel	Eshel Dramit	1982

M113 BARDELAS

Armoured Personnel Carrier
Gepanzerter Mannschaftstransportwagen

The IDF is, after the US Army, the major user of the M113 Armoured Personnel Carrier. Some 5,500-6,000 of the vehicles have been supplied. The M113 is known officially at least, as the "Bardelas" (Cheetah) in Israeli service. "Zelda" the early nickname for the machine has almost faded out of use. The most common term used for the M113 is "Nagmash" (acronym for Noseh Guysot Meshoryan), which simply means Armoured Personnel Carrier.

The vehicle entered into service in 1972, just in time to experience combat, primarily on the Egyptian front, in the Yom-Kippur War of October 1973. The M113 earned a reputation within the IDF for being mechanically reliable and agile. Unfortunately the 1982 Lebanon War underlined the fact that the M113 was terribly vulnerable to Soviet-made RPGs. Consequently Israeli industry has made great efforts to improve on the baseline protection offered by the M113. Appliqué armour packs, effective against threats ranging from 14.5mm rounds right up to add-on armour capable of defeating RPG warheads have been introduced. The M113 has been converted for many specialised tasks within the IDF. In recent years the Israelis have been involved in low key warfare against the Palestinians. Consequently rather ugly but effective superstructures of various types have been added to the roof of the M113. These are useful for protecting the crew and passengers of the M113 and can defeat the range of projectiles and incendiaries associated with low intensity warfare.

Despite its active service life of now more than thirty years, the M113 Nagmash "Bardelas" will continue to soldier on within the IDF for the near future.

Die Israelische Armee, IDF, ist nach den USA der Hauptnutzer des M113 Mannschaftstransportwagens. Etwa 5.500-6.000 dieser Fahrzeuge sind insgesamt an Israel geliefert worden. Offiziell wird der M113 im Dienste der IDF als „Bardelas" (Jagdleopard) bezeichnet. Der frühere Spitzname „Zelda" wird kaum noch verwendet. Die genaue hebräische Bezeichnung für den M113 ist „Nagmash" (Noseh Guysot Meshoryan), was für gepanzerter Mannschaftstransportwagen steht.

Das Fahrzeug wurde 1972 in den aktiven Dienst übernommen, gerade rechtzeitig, um im Yom-Kippur Krieg vom Oktober 1973 zum Einsatz zu kommen. Der M113 erwarb sich schnell den Ruf als mechanisch zuverlässiges und hochbewegliches Fahrzeug. Der Krieg im Libanon 1982 unterstrich jedoch auf signifikante Weise die Verwundbarkeit des Fahrzeugs gegenüber sowjetischen Panzerfäusten vom Typ RPG-7. Als Reaktion darauf ergriff die israelische Industrie umfassende Maßnahmen um den M113 besser zu schützen. Zusatzpanzerungselemente steigerten den Panzerschutz bis zum Kaliber 14,5 mm und gegen Panzerfäuste.

Der M113 wird in der IDF in zahlreichen Umbauten für viele Spezialaufgaben eingesetzt. Besonders der Kampf während der Palästinenserunruhen führte zu einigen, nicht gerade schön aussehenden aber hocheffektiven, Umbauten, die den Schutz der Besatzung und aufgesessenen Infanterie verbesserten und nun weitreichenderen Schutz in den Konflikten niedriger Intensität garantieren.

Trotz seiner aktiven Dienstzeit von nunmehr über dreißig Jahren wird der M113 Nagmash "Bardelas" weiterhin eine der Stützen der israelischen Armee auch in der nächsten Zukunft bleiben.

M113 Nagmash - The workhorse of the infantry. So many M113s have been converted to specialised roles, or have been upgraded or given appliqué armour, it is worthwhile remembering that many hundreds of M113s still remain in an untouched condition as delivered from the U.S. and with only minor modifications such as exhaust shields, and external stowage racks and boxes. The baseline M113 does not fully match the modern IDF's operational requirements as far as survivability is concerned. However, given financial restrictions, the IDF has no possibility of replacing the M113 for the foreseeable future. At best, the vehicles will be modernised.

M113 Nagmash - Das Arbeitspferd der Infanterieeinheiten. Obwohl so viele M113 für spezielle Aufgabenbereiche umgebaut worden sind, verblieben doch viele Hundert in der amerikanischen Ursprungsversion, wenn auch mit minimalen Anpassungen wie Auspuffverkleidung sowie externen Halterungen und Staukästen. Der prinzipielle Aufbau des M113 ist den modernen israelischen Anforderungen an ein geschütztes Fahrzeug und in Sachen Überlebensfähigkeit im Gefecht nicht mehr gewachsen. Dennoch werden finanzielle Einschränkungen den M113 auch in der näheren Zukunft im aktiven Dienst verbleiben lassen. Im besten Falle stände wohl eine Modernisierung an. (Both IDF Spokesperson Unit Yiftach Ofek)

The M113 was the first real modern battle taxi, developed to transport infantry and support units on the modern mechanized battlefield. It is fitted with a two-stroke six-cylinder Detroit diesel engine. The relatively weak aluminium armour makes it vulnerable to enemy RPG and anti-tank guided missile fire. Only up-armoured versions of the M113 will be sent into urban warfare by the IDF.

Der M113 war der erste wirkliche gepanzerte Mannschafttransportwagen der dazu dienen konnte, Infanterie- und Kampf-unterstützungseinheiten unter vollem Panzerschutz auf ein modernes mechanisiertes Gefechtsfeld zu führen. Das Fahrzeug ist mit einem 6-Zylinder Dieselmotor ausgestattet. Seine relativ dünne Aluminiumnpanzerung ist besonders empfindlich gegenüber gegnerischem RPG- und Panzerabwehrlenkflugkörper-Beschuss. So werden nur aufgepanzerte Varianten des M113 von der IDF für den Kampf in bebautem Gelände genutzt.
(Both IDF Spokesperson Unit Yiftach Ofek)

The Israeli M113 from rear. Note the clean interior after a maintainance shift at the Southern Command near Beer Sheva. The interior of the machine is painted the standard pale green typical of the M113 family in Israeli service. Note the external storage panniers mounted to the rear and flanks of the vehicle. The vehicles are all camouflaged in Israeli standard "Chameleon Olive".

Der israelische M113 von hinten. Man beachte den hier nach ausgiebiger Reinung sehr sauberen Kampfraum im T-Bereich des Süd-Kommandos in Ber-Sheeba. Die Innenraumfarbe, Blassgrün, ist typisch für den Einsatz in der israelischen Armee. Man beachte ebenfalls die typischen israelischen Staumöglichkeiten an den Seitenwänden der Wanne und am Fahrzeugheck. Die Fahrzeuge sind alle im IDF-typischen "Chamäleon-Oliv" getarnt.
(IDF Spokesperson Unit Yiftach Ofek)

These photographs were taken at night in a maintenance facility in 2005, one of the rare occasions the IDF has let a Western photographer so close to their active in-service vehicles. Note again the variety of stowage boxes on the M113 Nagmash, including the large one on the hull front. The standard-production M113 is built of aircraft quality aluminium which allows it to possess some of the same strengths as steel at a much lighter weight.

Diese Aufnahmen entstanden bei Nacht in einem Werkstattdepot der israelischen Streitkräfte im Jahre 2005 - eine der seltenen Gelegenheiten während derer ein westlicher Fotograf sich so freizügig Einsatzfahrzeugen der IDF nähern konnte. An diesen M113 Nagmash sind wieder die zahlreichen Staumöglichkeiten zu beachten, besonders hier auch an der Wannenfront. Die M113 der Standard-Fertigung führen eine Panzerung aus hochqualitativem Aluminium, dass eine enorme Gewichtsersparnis bei gleicher Stärke wie Panzerstahl bietet. (Author)

This M113 Nagmash is fitted with extensive sets of storage panniers and a tarpaulin carried on a roller bracket on the vehicle's roof.
Auch dieser M113 Nagmash zeigt wieder die typische Anhäufung von Staumöglichkeiten und führt am Dach zusätzlich Zeltstangen mit. (Author)

A Nagmash Chatap looking at its flank. This is a standard designation applied to those vehicles carrying a company's mechanics. As can be seen some of the storage pannier doors typical for this variant have been removed. Note also the fire extinguisher mounted on the vehicle's front next to a spare gear drive housing and the spare wheel on the rear roof.

Ein Nagmash Chatap in der Seitenansicht. Diese Bezeichnung wird allen Fahrzeugen zuteil, die von den Mechanikern einer Kompanie genutzt werden. An einigen der typischen großen Staukästen an der Wannenseite fehlt die Abdeckung. Man beachte auch den Feuerlöscher an der Fahrzeugfront neben einem Ersatz-Seitenvorgelege und die Ersatzlaufrolle hinten auf dem Turmdach. (Author)

The same M113 Nagmash Chatap equipped with the substantial set of storage panniers for carrying equipment and spares for mechanics, seen from the rear right. This view shows the tactical marking "9" on its side, the revolving chevron pointing to the front indicates the vehicle belongs to second company. Note the single white bar with black outline to enhance its visibility, painted on the rear hatch for station keeping when on the move at night. This particular vehicle has a front drive sprocket attached to its rear track guard.

Der gleiche M113 Nagmash Chatap in der Seitenansicht von hinten rechts. Die exzessiven Staukästen für die vielfältige Ausstattung und Ausrüstung der Mechaniker sind ein typisches Merkmal dieser Variante. Diese Perspektive erlaubt auch einen guten Blick auf die Markierungen: Das taktische Zeichen "9" an der Seite sowie das taktische "V", das hier nach vorne zeigt und so die Zugehörigkeit zur 2. Kompanie angibt. Der weiße Streifen mit schwarzem Rand über das Fahrzeugheck hat die Funktion der besseren Erkennbarkeit bei Kolonnenfahrten in der Nacht, ähnlich dem deutschen Leit-Tarnkreuz. Diese Fahrzeug hier hat ein Ersatz-Treibrad an der hinteren linken Kettenabdeckung montiert. (Author)

The same Nagmash Chatap from the front left. Note that the trim vane for amphibious operations has been replaced by an armoured plate. The rod, each side of the vehicle hull are to help give the commander and driver an idea of where the vehicle is when it negotiates narrow passages. This is necessary as the bulky storage panniers increase the vehicles footprint substantially. Note also the space for the exhaust pipe between the stowage boxes.

Der gleiche Nagmash Chatap in der Ansicht von vorne links. Das Schwallbrett für Wasserfahrt ist durch eine Panzerplatte ersetzt worden. Die Stäbe rechts und links der Oberwanne dienen als Orientierungshilfe für den Kommandanten und den Fahrer, da die zusätzlichen Staukästen die Einschätzung der Größe des Fahrzeugs an Engstellen sehr schwierig machen. Man beachte auch den freigelassenen Raum für das nach unten verlängerte Abgasrohr zwischen den Staukästen auf der rechten Wannenseite. (Author)

Nagmash Chatap looking at its rear. Note the stretchers stowed to the left edge of the machine.

Der Nagmash Chatap von hinten links. Man beachte die Trage für Verwundete an dem linken hinteren Staukasten. (Author)

Another Nagmash Chatap viewed from the front is shown here to illustrate the fact that even vehicles of the same type show numerous differences after some time in active use. This example is not fitted with an armour plate on the front. Note the spare track links now attached to the vehicle. The spinning chevron tactical mark belongs to the battalion's first company. Note the white tactical markings have a black shadow effect incorporated so they stand out more clearly.
Ein weiterer Nagmash Chatap in der Vorderansicht dient zur Verdeutlichung, wie sich auch Fahrzeuge der gleichen Bauart im Einzelfall unterscheiden können. Dieses spezifische Fahrzeug ist nicht mit der Panzerplatte an der Front ausgestattet, führt aber nun Ersatzkettenglieder. Man beachte das taktische "V" nach oben offen als Zeichen der 1. Kompanie des Bataillons. Die taktischen Markierungen heben sich durch einen schwarzen Schatteneffekt von der Grundfarbe ab um die Sichtbarkeit zu erhöhen. (Author)

The pictures were taken at the IDF Amour School in Shizafon in the Negev desert. Note the fuel cans mounted to the vehicles right rear and the Merkava 2 in the background.
Die Aufnahmen entstanden in der Israelischen Panzertruppenschule in Shizafon in der Negev-Wüste. Man beachte an diesem Fahrzeug die angebrachten Treibstoffkanister. Im Hintergrund ein Kampfpanzer Merkava 2. (**Author**)

The M113 Nagmash Chatap is used by mechanics down to company level of armoured and mechanised units. The Chatap units are responsible for everyday maintenance work, if the task requires a heavy lift capability, then work is allocated to the battalion M579 Fitter.
Der M113 Nagmash Chatap wird von den Mechanikern auf Kompanieebene der gepanzerten aund mechanisierten Einheiten genutzt. Chatap-Trupps führen die täglichen Wartungsaufgaben aus. Für größere Operationen wird ein M579 Fitter mit Kranaufbau hinzugezogen. (**Author**)

This Nagmash Chatap has a crudely hand-painted military vehicle registration plate. The interior of the vehicle is painted the standard pale green typical of the M113 family in IDF service.
Dieser Nagmash Chatap führt ein mit der Hand aufgemaltes Nummernschild. Das Fahrzeuginnere ist wiederum Blassgrün, wie bei allen anderen IDF M113 auch. (Author)

The particularly extensive set of storage panniers makes the machine considerably more bulky than the standard M113. Here with the large rear hatch closed.
Die vielen Staukästen machen den Chatap sehr viel schwieriger zu fahren als den Standard M113 Nagmash. Hier ein Chatap mit geschlossener Heckrampe.
(IDF Spokesperson Unit Yiftach Ofek)

The Nagmash Vayzata is the M113 fitted with appliqué TOGA armour. Note that the TOGA plating completely covers the front and flanks of the machine. The flanks of the vehicle above appear to show the remains of a material which has been eroded away from the underlying TOGA armour. The material may be polycarbonate, but its exact nature and function is unknown.

Der M113 mit der TOGA Abstandspanzerung wird als Nagmash Vayzata bezeichnet. Man beachte die TOGA Komponenten an der Fahrzeugfront und beiden Seiten. Auf einigen Segmenten hat sich bereits das ursprüngliche Deckmaterial, vermutlich ein Polykarbonat, abgelöst. Die genaue Funktion dieses Materials ist aber nicht bekannt. (Author)

The Nagmash Vayzata is much better protected than the standard Nagmash. The protection level granted by the stand-off TOGA armour permits the use of this vehicle in guerilla warfare in urban conflict. This Nagmash Vayzatas is used by combat engineers. Note the flags used for marking paths cut through minefields and the combat engineers tools that have been placed in the space between the TOGA and the machine's hull.

Der Nagmash Vayzata ist sehr viel besser gepanzert als der Standard M113 Nagmash. Der Grad des Panzerschutzes der TOGA Abstandspanzerung erlaubt die Nutzung dieses Fahrzeugs auch für den Kampf gegen irreguläre Kämpfer in bebautem Gebiet. Der hier abgbildete Nagmash Vayzata befindet sich im Dienste einer Einheit der Kampfpioniere. Man beachte die Flaggen zur Markierung von Minengassen sowie die umfangreiche Sonderausrüstung, die zwischen Wanne und TOGA-Panzerung verstaut wurde. (Author)

This Nagmash Vayzata with nearly factory-fresh TOGA armour plates consisting of perforated metal plating has been fitted with a Browning .50 calibre (12.7mm) heavy machine gun, here still fitted with its dust shroud. Note also the small aperture for the exhaust outlet.
Dieser Nagmash Vayzata führt eine fast neuwertige TOGA-Panzerung, die aus perforierten Platten besteht. Man beachte die Bewaffnung mit einem schweren .50 cal (12,7mm) Maschinengewehr, das auf diesem Foto aber zum Schutz gegen Staub abgedeckt ist. (**Author**)

In comparison, the front of this Nagmash Vayzata shows the result of hard use. Some of the TOGA panels have been bent out of shape and are not positioned accurately. The insulation surrounding the exhaust pipe extension has largely peeled off. Note that the driving light clusters have had their infra-red elements either removed or blanked off.
Im Vergleich ein Nagmash Vayzata, der schon bessere Tage gesehen hat. Einige der TOGA-Platten sind arg verbogen und nicht mehr genau platziert. Auch ist die Ummantelung des Auspuffrohrs schon stark verschlissen. Man beachte, dass die IR-Fahrlichtanlage fehlt. (**Author**)

This Nagmash Vayzata's tactical markings, from left to right indicate the following: The revolving chevron pointing to the front indicates second company. It is thought that the letter 1 indicates first platoon. The tactical symbol to the vehicles right is the sign designating combat engineer formations.

Die taktischen Zeichen an diesem Nagmash Vayzata haben folgende Bedeutung (auf der TOGA-Panzerung, von links nach rechts): Das zum Heck hin offene "V" zeigt die 2. Kompanie an, die Zahl "1" deutet auf den 1. Zug hin, das taktische Symbol am Heck bedeutet Kampfpioniere. (Author)

The TOGA armour denies highly visible application of markings by its perforated nature. This particular Nagmash Vayzata carries the tactical markings of a combat engineer unit just visible beneath the TOGA mesh on the rear of the vehicle. Note the hand-painted vehicle registration at the upper rear of the TOGA and the unidentifiable markings to the front.

Die perforierte TOGA-Panzerung macht die Anbringung von deutlich sichtbaren Markierungen schwierig. An diesem Nagmash Vayzata ist das taktische Zeichen der Kampfpioniere, am Heck unter dem mit der Hand aufgemalten Nummernschild, bereits kaum mehr zu erkennen. Die Markierungen am vorderen Teil der Panzerung sind bereits unleserlich. (Author)

The crew - who can be distinguished by their Type 602 ballistic helmets - amidst infantry passengers, pose for the author from the typically cluttered roof of a Nagmash Vayzata. The vehicle is armed with FN MAG 7.62mm machine guns and one heavy .50 cal (12.7mm) machine gun. Note the minefield marking rods sticking out of the side storage panniers.

Die Besatzung - die gut an ihren Typ 602 Panzerhelmen zu erkennen ist - umringt von aufgesessenen Infanteristen, posiert für den Autor von Dach eines typischen vollgepackten Nagmash Vayzata. Das Fahrzeug ist mit 7,62 mm FN MAG Maschinengewehren sowie einem schweren 12,7 mm Maschinengewehr bewaffnet. Man beachte wiederum die Flaggen zur Markierung von minenfreien Gassen, die außen am Fahrzeug verstaut sind. (Author)

On this Nagmash Vayzata the Polycarbonate covering of the perforated TOGA plating is mostly still intact. In the past the IDF made desperate efforts to improve the survivability of the M113 Nagmash. Perforated steel mesh armor screens were fitted to the flanks and front. The distance between the mesh screen and the main armour allows the fragments which have impacted to tumble and yaw.

An diesem Nagmash Vayzata ist die Polykarbonat-Beschichtung der perforiertern TOGA-Platten noch immer fast vollständig erhalten. Die Verbesserung des Panzerschutzes am M113 Nagmash war eines der wichtigsten Ziele der IDF Ingenieure in den vergangenen Jahren. Die Anbringung der perforierten Stahlplatten, die einschlagende Geschosse vor der eigentlichen Wannenpanzerung des Fahrzeugs ablenken bzw. zum Taumeln bringen und so die Durchschlagsleistung deutlich reduzieren, erwies sich als adäquate Maßnahme. (Author)

Another clear shot of a M113 Nagmash Vayzata without coating for direct comparison. The standard M113 Aluminium armour below the opened frontal maintenance hatches of the TOGA armour is visible.

Eine weitere klare Aufnahme eines M113 Nagmash Vayzata ohne die Beschichtung, zum direkten Vergleich. Unter den Zugangsklappen in der TOGA Panzerung an der Fahrzeugfront ist die gepanzerte Aluminium-Wanne des Basis-M113 gut zu erkennen. (Author)

TOGA in Detail - TOGA is made up of perforated ballistic steel and is fitted some 250mm away from the M113's baseline aluminium armour. TOGA stand-off armour is able to defeat armour piercing 14.5mm rounds and also has a degree of effectiveness against RPGs, detonating the rounds prematurely. "Vayzata" is the IDF's code name for machines fitted with perforated steel armour. "Vayzata" is a minor character from the bible.

TOGA im Detail - TOGA ist eine Abstands-Zusatzpanzerung aus Platten von perforiertem Panzerstahl, die etwa 250 mm von der eigentlichen Aluminium-Wannenpanzerung des M113 entfernt, nachträglich angebracht werden kann. TOGA kann Geschossen bis zu einem Kaliber von 14,5 mm widerstehen und reduziert die Einschlagsenergie von RPG-7 Panzerfaust-Geschossen so stark, dass die Basispanzerung des M113 nicht durchschlagen wird. "Vayzata" ist der Codename für alle IDF-Fahrzeuge, die mit dieser Panzerung nachgerüstet wurden, und stammt von einer Person aus der Bibel. (IDF Spokesperson Unit Yiftach Ofek + Author)

This command variant of the machine known as Nagmash Vayzata Pikud, has been fitted with an extendable mast, one often found amongst IDF units operating in a low intensity conflict area. It is possible that the mast is part of a system to block radio signals intended to detonate improvised explosive devices.

Die Kommando-Führungsvariante des M113 in der israelischen Armee wird als Nagmash Vayzata Pikud bezeichnet. Als besonderes Ausstattungsmerkmal ist der ausfahrbare Antennenmast zu erkennen. Der Nagmash Vayzata Pikud wird primär in Konflikten niedriger Intensität eingesetzt und es wird angenommen, dass die mitgeführte elektronische Ausstattung funkferngesteuerte Minenfallen stören kann.
(Author)

The same Nagmash Vayzata Pikud, seen from the other side. Note the extra antenna mounts along the side of the vehicle's roof.
Der gleiche Nagmash Vayzata Pikud von der anderen Seite aus gesehen. Man beachte die umfangreiche Ausstattung mit Antennenfüßen auf dem Fahrzeugdach. (Author)

The Nagmash Vayzata Pikud from the rear. Note the untidy clutter of materiel that has been placed in the space between the TOGA and the machine's hull. The exact purpose of the wire reels on the vehicle's roof is unknown; they may be associated with a tactical telephone system. Note the ungainly storage pannier to the vehicle's rear. The tarpaulin carried on a roller bracket on the vehicle's roof, presumably when open, for use in creating a work area partially protected from sun and rain.

Der Nagmash Vayzata Pikud in der Heckansicht. Deutlich ist wiederum die Nutzung des Raumes zwischen der Wanne und der Zusatzpanzerung als Stauraum zu erkennen. Der genaue Zweck der Kabeltrommeln auf dem Dach ist nicht bekannt, vermutlich sind sie Teil eines Feldtelefon-Systems. Bemerkenswert sind die groß dimensionierten, fast klobigen, Staukästen und -flächen am Heck. Die Plane rechts oben auf dem Dach ist auf Rollen montiert, damit schnell ein Sonnen- bzw. Regenschutz aufgebaut werden kann. (Author)

The M113 Nagman grew out of the fighting in southern Lebanon against the guerrillas of Hezbollah. The IDF were using the M113 Nagmash Vayzata as a patrol vehicle during the low intensity conflict (LIC) against their agile enemy. The M113s roof mounted machine guns were of considerable use against ambushes, but the machine gun operators were increasingly vulnerable manning their weapons. The Nagman consists of a superstructure offering a degree of protection to the vehicle commander and plates with vision blocks to protect the upper body of infantrymen standing upright and taking station in the roof hatches. In its early stages the Nagman commander's superstructure was open to the back, protection in the rear being provided by the open commander's hatch. In recent years the commander's open hexagon of armoured plates has become fully enclosed, with a full rear plate and roof. To an extent, situational awareness has been downgraded in favour of protection.

Der M113 Nagman entstand aus den Lehren der Gefechte im Süd-Libanon mit Hisbollah Milizen. Die dort in einem Konflikt niedriger Intensität gegen einen hochmobilen Gegner eingesetzten M113 Nagmash Vayzata zeigten besondere Verwundbarkeit für die Bediener der auf dem Fahrzeugdach montierten Maschinengewehre. Der Nagman bietet nun durch den gepanzerten zusätzlichen Aufbau einen höheren Grad an Schutz für den Fahrzeugkommandanten und die aufgesessene Infanterie, zumindest bis Brusthöhe. Frühe Baulose des Nagman hatten einen nach hinten nur durch die Kommandantenluke geschützen Aufbau für den Kommandanten. Neuere Baulose führen hier einen Rundum-Panzerschutz einschließlich Dachpanzerung. Unter Akzeptanz dieser deutlichen Verbesserungen im Panzerschutz wurde beim Nagman der Überblick über das nähere Gefechtsfeld jedoch erheblich reduziert. (Author)

This flank view of the M113 Nagman shows the armour plates with accompanying vision blocks, fitted to the M113 to adopt it to LIC warfare. Armour plates have been provided to protect infantry standing in the vehicles rear. The superstructure to the front of the vehicle's roof has been built to protect the vehicles commander. The vehicle is also equipped with the TOGA armour.
Seitenansicht des M113 Nagman. Die Panzerkuppel für den Kommandanten und die gepanzerten Luken mit Panzerglas-Sichtblöcken für die aufgesessene Infanterie sind deutlich zu erkennen. Das Fahrzeuge trägt zusätzlich eine TOGA-Panzerung an der Wanne.
(Author)

A close up of the armoured hatch fitted with vision blocks, used to protect the heads and upper bodies of infantrymen standing in the rear hatch. Note the massive rubber buffers intended to protect the vision blocks from impact damage when the hatch is moved from the vertical to the fully lowered position.
Nahaufnahme der schweren gepanzerten Luken mit Panzerglas-Sichtscheiben, die die aufgesessene Infanterie bis zu einem gewissen Grad vor gegnerischem Feuer schützen soll. Man beachte auch die massiven Stopper, die beim Umlegen der Platten das Panzerglas schützen sollen.
(Author)

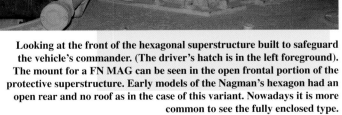

Looking at the front of the hexagonal superstructure built to safeguard the vehicle's commander. (The driver's hatch is in the left foreground). The mount for a FN MAG can be seen in the open frontal portion of the protective superstructure. Early models of the Nagman's hexagon had an open rear and no roof as in the case of this variant. Nowadays it is more common to see the fully enclosed type.
Blick auf den sechseckigen gepanzerten Aufbau für den Kommandanten. Vorne links im Bild die Fahrerluke. Seitlich am Aufbau ist eine Halterung für ein 7,62 mm FN MAG Maschinengewehr zu sehen. Frühe Nagman Baulose hatten noch keine Panzerung für das Dach und den hinteren Bereich des Kommandanten, wie hier zu sehen. Mittlerweile sind die rundum gepanzerten Baulose aber sehr häufig. (Author)

A M113 Kasman undergoing maintenance at an ordnance base. The engine was already removed. Note the monstrous armoured superstructure of this vehicle in comparison to the M113 Nagman. Kasman being the acronym for "Kesem a Mangina" meaning as much as "The Charm Of Music".

Ein M113 Kasman wird gewartet, der Motor ist bereits entfernt worden. Man beachte den übergroßen gepanzerten Aufbau auf der Wanne, der sich deutlich vom M113 Nagman unterscheidet. Das hebräische Wort Kasman ist ein Akronym für "Kesem a Mangina" und bedeutet soviel wie "Betörende Musik". (Author)

The M113 Kasman was a response by the IDF to improve the protection of APCs committed to fighting the Palestinian Intifada. Like the fight against Hezbollah guerrillas on the Lebanese border, the Intifada could be classified as a low intensity conflict (LIC). However, the Intifada was fought in a largely urban environment and the nature of the weaponry used by the IDF's opponents was different. Sniper fire and Molotov cocktails were more likely to be encountered than ATGMs or RPGs. Consequently the IDF built a more substantial, roofed superstructure on top of some of its M113s, more substantial than that provided by the Nagman. The Kasman encloses both the commander's position and that of the passenger roof hatches. The ugly structure, often referred to by the nickname "dog house", incorporates both vision blocks and firing ports.

Der M113 Kasman stellt die Reaktion der israelischen Streitkräfte auf die palästinensische Intifada dar. Wie auch für den Kampf gegen die Hisbollah Milizen wurde eine stark verbesserte Panzerung benötigt. Trotz der Tatsache, dass auch die Intifada als ein Konflikt niedriger asymmetrischer Intensität bezeichnet werden kann, unterscheidet sie sich jedoch vom asymmetrischen Konflikt mit der Hisbollah durch das vermehrte Gefecht in stark bebautem Gelände. Somit unterschied sich auch die Waffenausstattung des Gegners: Scharfschützenfeuer und Molotow-Brandflaschen sind sehr viel wahrscheinlicher als Panzerfäuste oder Panzerabwehrlenkflugkörper. Daraus resultierend wurde beim M113 Kasman sehr viel stärkerer Wert auf eine Dachpanzerung gelegt als z.B. beim M113 Nagman. Direkt erkennbar ist die unterschiedliche Konzeption an den auch nach oben gepanzerten Positionen für den Kommandanten und die aufgesessene Infanterie. Der ästhetisch sicherlich nicht besonders anprechende gepanzerte Aufbau auf der Fahrzeugwanne wird oft als "Hundehütte" bezeichnet und umfasst Panzerglas-Sichtscheiben und Schießluken. (Author)

A rather forlorn looking M113 Kasman, its TOGA armour partially removed in order to allow access to the baseline vehicle structure and engine.
An diesem Kasman ist die TOGA-Panzerung für Wartungsarbeiten teilweise entfernt bzw. abgeklappt worden. (Author)

A close up of the Kasman "dog house". The superstructure has an almost medieval appearance, belied by its ballistic glass vision blocks and firing ports for MAG machine-gunners.
Nahaufnahme des gepanzerten Aufbaus, auch "Hundehütte" genannt, des Kasman. Die Form des gepanzerten Aufbaus ähnelt sehr einer mittelalterlichen Befestigungsanlage, jedoch mit modernster Schutztechnik wie beschußsicherem Panzerglas und Schießluken für die MG-Schützen. (Author)

In 2005 a new variation of the M113 optimised for low intensity conflict began to appear in service. Like the Kasman, the new Kasman Maoz armoured superstructure covered both the commander's position and that of the passenger roof hatches. However this time the superstructure fitted to the vehicle roof is angled to improve ballistic protection and the general shape is more streamlined and less bulky. On the Kasman Maoz (Strongpoint) protective superstructure, the number of vision blocks and firing points are reduced when compared to the original Kasman.

Im Jahre 2005 wurde eine neue, und weiter für den Guerillakrieg verbesserte, Variante des M113 eingeführt. Wie bereits der Kasman, zeigte der neue Kasman Maoz ("Festung") einen rundum geschlossenen Panzeraufbau für Kommandant und aufgesessene Infanterie. Neu war jedoch, dass die Seitenwände des Aufbaus nun geneigt waren um einen besseren ballistischen Schutz zu garantieren. Auch ist der gesamte Aufbau nun sehr viel stromlinienförmiger und die Anzahl der Sichtblöcke und Schießluken, im Vergleich zum Kasman, wurde reduziert. (Author)

A close up of what appears to be a bullet impact on one of the Kasman Maoz vision blocks which resists up to 7.62mm shots. Below an open firing port.
Details der bis 7,62 mm beschußsicheren Panzerglasscheiben. Man beachte den Treffer. Darunter eine offene Schießluke. (Author)

Looking up at the front of the M113 Kasman Maoz. Note, IMI CL-3030 instantaneous smoke grenade launchers, each with ten grenades, are fitted to each side of the machine.
Vorderansicht des Panzeraufbaus. An der Wannenfront einer der beiden IMI CL-3030 Nebelmittelwurfanlagen für je zehn Patronen. (Author)

Two Kasman Maoz undergoing maintenance at an Israeli Army ordnance base.
Zwei Kasman Maoz während Wartungsarbeiten auf einem Stützpunkt der israelischen Armee. (Author)

The IDF use the M113 Nagmash also as an Armored Medical Evacuation Vehicle AMEV for wounded soldiers. The vehicle used is usually of a basic, standard M113 configuration. On occasion they can be seen with appliqué TOGA armour packs. Note this ambulance M113 Nagmash Ambulance AMEV variant only has one of the external fuel tanks fitted. Note the Red Shield of David ambulance marking.
Die IDF nutzt den M113 Nagmash auch in der Variante Sanitätspanzer. In dieser Nutzung sind nur wenige israelische Umbauten an der amerikanischen Grundvariante zu finden. Manche dieser Fahrzeuge sind aber mit der TOGA Panzerung nachgerüstet worden. Der hier abgebildete M113 Nagmash Ambulanz, mit rotem Davidstern als Erkennungszeichen, führt nur einen der beiden Treibstoff-Zusatztanks am Heck montiert. (Author)

This M113 Nagmash used as an evacuation vehicle, note the "Magan David Adom" (Red Shield of David) symbol also to be found on the inner side of the roof hatch. Improvements in medical capabilities include an on-board oxygen production unit and improved litter configuration. As with all other Israeli military vehicles, too, all vital areas important for regular maintenance or immediate accessibility are marked in bright red.
Der M113 Nagmash Amulanz von innen. Man beachte den "Magan David Adom" - den roten Davidstern als Zeichen für ein Sanitätsfahrzeug, der hier auch auf der Innenseite der Dachluke zu sehen ist. Die medizinische Zusatzaustattung dieses Fahrzeugs beinhaltet modernste Sauerstoff-Erzeugung im Fahrzeug und verbesserte Anbringung der Krankentragen. Wie auch bei allen anderen israelischen Militärfahrzeugen sind alle wichtigen Bereiche der regelmäßigen Wartung oder Kontrolle bzw. der notwendigen schnellen Erkennbarkeit in Rot markiert.
(IDF Spokesperson Unit Yiftach Ofek)

The M113 based M579 Fitter vehicle is used within the IDF at battalion level. The recovery vehicle is designated to the battalion HQ of tank and mechanised units. The Fitter, modified from the US original by the addition of numerous external packs and storage panniers, is equipped with a 6,800 lbs capacity crane. Again, those parts which require regular maintenance and/or lubrication are painted red. Note the external panniers.

Der auf dem M113 basierende Berge/ Kranpanzer M579 Fitter wird von der israelischen Armee in Werkstatteinheiten auf Bataillonsebene der Panzertruppe oder bei mechanisierten Einheiten genutzt. Dort ist es direkt dem Bataillons-Hauptquartier unterstellt. Bereits in der amerikanischen Grundvariante finden sich am M579 zahlreiche externe Staukästen, sowie der unübersehbare Kran mit einer maximalen Hebelast von 3.087 kg. Auch am M579 sind die regelmäßigen Wartungs- und Schmierpunkte in Rot markiert.
(Author)

Like other users of the M113, the IDF has purchased a number of M577 command post vehicles, known in the IDF as the Mugaf. Externally they remain very close to the US originals, other than the Israeli propensity to fit additional external storage racks, and baskets to all their AFVs. On the inside the M577 Mugaf is equipped with a wide variety of communications and other electronic equipment. Further details are secret, thus the M577 Mugaf is a rarely photographed type in IDF vehicle inventory.

Wie auch andere Nationen, die den M113 nutzen, hat die israelische Armee das M577 Kommando-/Führungsfahrzeug auf diesen Fahrgestell beschafft. In der IDF ist der M577 als Mugaf bekannt. Vom Äußerlichen her ist der M577 der israelischen Armee der amerikanishcen Standardversion sehr ähnlich, natürlich wieder mit Ausnhame der exzessiven Anbringung von Staukästen. Die umfangreiche Funk- und Fernmeldeaustattung im Inneren unterliegt jedoch der Geheimhaltung, weshalb Fotos des M577 Mugaf sehr selten sind.
(IDF Spokesperson Unit Yiftach Ofek)

The rear of a M577 Mugaf. The raised hull to allow the command crew a standing position is clearly evident from his perspective. Map boards, radios, and crew seats could be installed in the passenger compartment.
Heckansicht des M577 Mugaf. Die erhöhte Wanne, um der Führungsmannschaft während der Arbeit eine stehende Position zu ermöglichen, ist klar zu erkennen. Im Innenraum finden sich neben der elektronischen und Funk-Austattung auch Kartentische und Sitzbänke.
(IDF Spokesperson Unit Yiftach Ofek)

The M577 Mugaf from the rear and side. Note the external storage panniers mounted to the rear and flanks of the machine. The two empty storage brackets towards the top of the sides are for fire extinguishers. The basket in front of the raised superstructure holds an external power generating unit. In front of that basket the exhaust outlet for the generator. Note the very large markings.
Der M577 Mugaf von hinten und von der Seite. Man beachte die zahlreichen Staumöglichkeiten an der Außenwänden der Wannenpanzerung. Die zwei leeren Halterungen nahe dem oberen Dachrand dienen der Aufnahme von Feuerlöschern. Im Korb vor dem erhöhten gepanzerten Aufbau ist eine externes Stromerzeugeraggregat untergebracht. Vor dem Korb die Auspuffanlage des Generators. Man beachte auch die ungewöhnlich großen Markierungen. (IDF Spokesperson Unit Yiftach Ofek)

Walk-around a M577 Mugaf showing many of the specific Israeli additions to this vehicle in IDF service.
Rundgang um einen M577 Mugaf, der die zahlreichen israelischen Modifikationen an diesem Fahrzeug der IDF darstellt. (Author)

Walk-around the same M577 Mugaf showing many of the specific Israeli additions to this vehicle in IDF service.
Rundgang um den gleichen M577 Mugaf, der die zahlreichen israelischen Modifikationen an diesem Fahrzeug der IDF darstellt. (Author)

T-54/55 ACHZARIT

Armoured Infantry Assault Carrier
Gepanzertes Gefechtsfahrzeug der Infanterie

In the wake of the 1982 Lebanon War and the casualties inflicted on their mechanised infantry mostly equipped with the M113 Nagmash, the IDF re-evaluated the expeted role and actual performance of their infantry carriers. They concluded that an Armored Personnel Carrier, by virtue of its function, is exposed to greater risk than a tank. Given their extreme sensitivity to casualties, caused by lack of manpower, the Israelis wanted a better protected vehicle than the M113. The IDF sought a heavy Armoured Personnel- and Assault Carrier and were forced to develop it from scratch. Only previsted huge expenses and the need to prioritise Merkava hulls for only use as tanks prevented a Merkava based heavy assault vehicle.

A much cheaper solution was found in the IDF storage depots. There, since 1967, the Israelis held many hundreds of captured T-54/55 tanks. Some of these tanks were successively upgraded and entered into israeli service as the Tiran 4 and Tiran 5 tank. Using these hulls the Achzarit was born.

The engine of the Achzarit is mounted transversely. The crew of three are seated at the front of the machine. Normally seven infantrymen are carried. The Achzarit does not have the turret or other cannon as a standard AIFV. His standard weapon is the 7.62mm machine gun. It is estimated that approx. 200 examples of the heavy assault carrier are in service.

However, the Achzarit active service has been limited to low intensitiy conflicts in Gaza and against Hezbollah fighters in southern Lebanon. The highest profile of the Achzarit during the Palestinian Intifada (insurgency) came in the year 2002, when a large number of this machines participated in the impressive raid on Palestinian President Yassir Araft´s headquarter in Ramallah.

With now true Armoured Infantry Fighing vehicle in the classic sense fielded by the IDF, the Achzarit is a capable specialised machine albeit with the lack of a medium calibre automated gun as in its Western and Eastern counterparts.

Nach dem Libanon Krieg von 1982 und den dort erlittenen Verlusten in den mechansisierten und meist mit M113 Nagmash ausgestatteten Infanterieeinheiten, war die IDF gezwungen, die Rolle eines Kampffahrzeugs der Infanterie neu zu überdenken. Das Resultat war die Erkenntnis, dass ein gepanzerter Mannschaftstransportwagen weit stärker gegnerischem Feuer ausgesetzt war, als ein Kampfpanzer. Unter Hinblick auf die numerisch geringe Bevölkerungszahl Israels und der daher besonders hohen Empfindlichkeit gegenüber personellen Verlusten, musste ein Nachfolger für den M113 in der Rolle eines gut gepanzerten Fahrzeugs für die Infanterie gefunden werden. Die zu hohen Kosten und zu geringen Fertigungskapazitäten erlaubten nicht, Merkava Wannen für diesen Zweck heranzuziehen.

Eine preisgünstigere Lösung wurde in den eingemotteten Kampfpanzern T-54/55 gefunden, die zu Hunderten erbeutet und als Kriegsreserve in Tiran 4 und Tiran 5 umgebaut, in den Depots lagerten. Man entfernte den Turm und panzerte die Wanne zusätzlich - der Achzarit war geboren.

Der Motor des Achzarit ist quer eingebaut, die Besatzung besteht aus drei Mann plus sieben Infanteristen. Der Achzarit besitzt keinen Turm wie ein normaler Schützenpanzer, sondern ist nur mit 7,62 mm Maschinengewehren bewaffnet. Etwa 200 der Achzarit „Sturmpanzer der Infanterie" befinden sich vermutlich im Dienst.

Der Einsatzbereich des Achzarit ist jedoch auf Konflikte niedriger Intensität wie im Gaza-Streifen oder gegen die Hisbollah-Milizen im Südlibanon begrenzt. Den Höhepunkt der Nutzung des Achzarit im Gefecht bildete der Einsatz während der palästinensischen Intifada im Jahre 2002, als eine große Anzahl dieser Fahrzeuge an der beeindruckenden Erstürmung des Amtssitzes des Palästinenserpräsidenten Jassir Arafat in Ramallah teilnahm.

Mit dem Achzarit führt die IDF ein kampfstarkes und gut gepanzertes Fahrzeug für die Infanterieeinheiten, jedoch keinen Schützenpanzer in klassischen Sinne. Hier ist das Fehlen einer automatischen Kanone mittleren Kalibers deutlich zu spüren.

One of the outcomes of the Lebanon War was the IDF decision to build a heavy armored infantry vehicle, the Achzarit. About 250 were build, 200 of which are still in active service. They are intended to supplement the old M113 carriers, espacially in urban warfare environments. The Achzarit is an ingenious heavy carrier developed by the Israelis upon the hulls of captured T-54 and T-55 tanks. The old tanks have their turrets removed and are rebuilt with a new power pack to allow rear access for the infantry. The Achzarit is fitted with over 14 tonnes of advanced armour, on top of the T-55 hull's baseline protection. This makes it the most survivable carrier in service. The Achzarit is intended for use in Combined Arms operations. Its excellent protection allows it to operate on the front-line, alongside Merkava tanks. Note the Rafael overhead weapon system fitted with a 7.62mm machine gun directly in front of the vehicle commander. The machine gun can be aimed, operated and fired from under armour when the vehicle is buttoned up.

Eine der wichtigsten Erkenntnisse des Libanon Krieges von 1982 war die Notwendigkeit, ein schwer gepanzertes Kampffahrzeug für die Infanterie zu entwickeln - den Achzarit. Etwa 250 wurden gebaut, von denen noch immer rund 200 im aktiven Dienst stehen sollen. Der Achzarit soll die mit M113 ausgestatteten Einheiten verstärken, besonders für den Einsatz in stark bebautem Gebiet. Der Achzarit stellt ein einmaliges und sehr innovatives Konzept dar, das auf den Wannen von T-54 und T-55 Kampfpanzern beruht, von denen man die Türme entfernt hatte. Im weiteren wurde ein neuer Motor eingebaut um infanteristische Zugangsmöglichkeiten im Heck zu schaffen. Die neue Panzerung schlägt mit 14 Tonnen zusätzlich zur Kampfpanzer-Grundpanzerung zu Buche. Somit hat der Achzarit im Gefecht die wahrscheinlich höchste Überlebensfähigkeit aller vergleichbaren Fahrzeugtypen. Seine exzellente Panzerung erlaubt es dem Achzarit, dem Merkava ins Gefecht zu folgen. Die Bewaffnung besteht jedoch nur aus 7,62 mm Maschinengewehren, eines davon in der, unter Panzerschutz zu bedienenden, Rafael OWS Waffenstation vor dem Kommandanten. (Marsh Gelbart)

An Achzarit returns to base in the Negev desert, around 1997. The commander and the gunner are female instructors in training. Note that the Rafael OWS is missing its 7.62mm machine gun.
Ein Achzarit auf dem Rückmarsch zum Heimatstützpunkt in der Negev-Wüste, etwa 1997. Kommandant und Richtschütze sind weibliche Ausbilder. Man beachte die Rafael OWS Waffenstation, jedoch ohne eingebautes 7,62 mm Maschinengewehr. (Marsh Gelbart)

A total of ten soldiers are carried, with the driver being seated at the front left with the vehicle commander and gunner to his right. The driver is provided with four day periscopes with an additional six being provided in the rear troop compartment.

Insgesamt zehn Soldaten finden im Achzarit Platz. Der Fahrer sitzt vorne links und der Kommandant und der Richtschütze rechts. Dem Fahrer stehen vier Tageslicht-Periskope zur Verfügung, weitere sechs befinden sich über dem hinteren Kampfraum. (Marsh Gelbart)

The Achzarit´s main failing is that it is relatively under-powered. The IDF has not been entirely happy with the vehicle due its sluggish automotive perfomance compared to IDF tanks.

Der einzige Nachteil des Achzarit ist das zu geringe Gewichts-/Leistungs-Verhältnis. Die IDF ist generell nicht mit dem für modernste Ansprüche ungenügenden Antrieb zufrieden.
(Marsh Gelbart)

The seven infantrymen are seated to the rear. Access to the rear has been achived by mounting a new engine transversely, thus creating space for an armoured infantry access hatch. Note the additional external storage net.

Die sieben Infanteristen befinden sich im Heck des Fahrzeugs. Um hier Zugang zu schaffen, wurde der neue Motor querliegend eingebaut, was die Montage einer gepanzerten Zugangsluke für die Infanterie ermöglichte. Man beachte das externe Staunetz.
(Marsh Gelbart)

The rear flanks of the machine are fitted with TOGA perforated steel appliqué armour. There is a space between the hull and TOGA sheets which is used for external stowage. The TOGA sheets are cut and hinged in order to provide access to material stored between the TOGA and the hull. Note the red painted hinges. The former T-54/55 main battle tanks can only be identified by the roadwheel assembly. Even the engine deck has been replaced with a Centurion deck.

Der seitliche Heckbereich der Wanne ist mit der TOGA-Panzerung aus perforiertem Stahlblech versehen. Der Raum zwischen der TOGA-Panzerung und der Wannenpanzerung wird als Stauraum für Ausrüstung genutzt. Um hier den Zugang zu vereinfachen sind die TOGA-Platten an Scharnieren befestigt - die roten Griffe zum Öffnen sind gut zu erkennen. Das Basisfahrzeug, der Kampfpanzer T-54/55, ist nur noch am Fahrwerk zu erkennen. Selbst das Motordeck wurde ersetzt, hier durch Baugruppen des Centurion Kampfpanzers. (Marsh Gelbart)

The Achzarit has a combat loaded weight of 44 tons compared to the 36 tons of a T-54/55 main battle tank. While the T-55 turret has been removed from the Achzarit, most of the difference in weight between the present Achzarit 44 tons and the 27 tons of the T-55 hull is accounted for by the additional armour protection for improved battlefield survivability. Note that the Rafael overhead weapon system, to the front of the vehicle's roof, has had its machine gun removed from its mount.

Der Achzarit hat ein Gefechtsgewicht von 44 Tonnen im Vergleich zu den 36 Tonnen des Kampfpanzers T-54/55. Wenn man vom T-55 den Turm entfernt, wiegt die Wanne nur noch 27 Tonnen. Die Masse der 17 Tonnen Gewichtsunterschied zum Achzarit macht dessen Zusatzpanzerung aus. Man beachte an diesem Fahrzeug, dass das MG in der OWS nicht montiert ist. (Paulus v. Wijk)

Another look onto the rear of the Achzarit, same vehicle as above, shows more details of the armoured infantry access hatch and the large stowage net. A close look on the lower hull shows details of the rear of the T-54/55 main battle tank.

Eine weitere Achzarit Heckansicht, das gleiche Fahrzeug wie oben, zeigt die gepanzerte Zugangsluke für die Infantrie rechts, und links davon das übergroße Staunetz. Bei genauerem Hinsehen sind unten an der Fahrzeugwanne Details des T-54/55 zu erkennen.

(Paulus v. Wijk)

Top view on the engine deck and upper side of the infantry access hatch, same vehicle as on the previous side. *Draufsicht auf das Motordeck und die Infanterieluke, gleiches Fahrzeug wie auf der vorherigen Seite.* (Paulus v. Wijk)

The Achzarit left side. The front of the machine has a six round IMI CL-3030 grenade launcher fitted to each flank. While the five roadwheels, drive sprocket and idler of the T-54/55 have been retained, the wheels are now sprung by new torsion bars which allow a greater wheel travel, with the first and last wheel stations being fitted with an hydraulic bump stop. This suspension upgrade provides the vehicle with better cross-country mobility and allows it to operate with main battle tanks.

Der Achzarit von links gesehen. Vorne am Fahrzeug finden sich IMI CL-3030 Nebelmittel-wurfanlagen mit sechs Schuss zu jeder Seite. Das Fahrwerk besteht aus den T-54/55-typischen fünf Laufrollen, Leitrad vorne und Treibrad hinten. Das Fahrwerk ist auf Drehstab-Federung umgebaut worden, das der ersten und letzten Laufrolle mehr Spiel erlaubt. Ebenfalls wurde ein hydraulischer Endanschlagsdämpfer montiert. Alles in allem erlaubt das bessere Fahrwerk gesteigerte Geländegängigkeit um mit den Kampfpanzern mithalten zu können. (Paulus v. Wijk)

The impressive rear access hatch in open position. One of potential disadvantage of this design is that when the ramp is raised, it indicates to an enemy that troops are about to disembark.
Die beeindruckende Heckluke für die Infanterie in geöffneter Position. Einer der größten Nachteile dieser Konstruktionslösung ist die Tatsache, dass die offene Luke schon von weitem gut erkennbar ist, und somit den abgesesessenen Einsatz der Infanterie sofort anzeigt. (**Marsh Gelbart**)

Full speed! The Achzarit engine is based on that used by the M109 self-propelled gun, widely employed by the IDF. This eases maintenance and spare-part supply significantly.
Mit Vollgas voraus! Der Motor des Achzarit wurde von der Panzerhaubitze M109 übernommen, die in der IDF weit verbreitet ist. Diese Tatsache vereinfacht den Wartungsaufwand und die Ersatzteilbeschaffung erheblich. (IDF Spokesperson Unit Helena Moshe)

PUMA, NAGMASHOT, NAGMACHON, NAGMACHON-MIFLESET, NAKPADON

Centurion-based Armoured Engineer Vehicles / Infantry Assault Carrier
Gepanzerte Infanterie-Sturmfahrzeuge / Pionierpanzer auf Basis Centurion

The 1982 Lebanon War brought home to the Israelis that they needed highly survivable combat engineer vehicles (CEV), capable of clearing a path through natural and man made obstacles, and heavily armoured infantry carriers. The Centurion tank was withdrawn from IDF front-line service in the late 1980s; this provided a source of hulls upon which a new vehicles could be built.

The IDFs LIC carriers came into use in the early 1980s. After the Lebanon War of 1982, the IDF built a series of different infantry carriers using the converted hulls of Centurion tanks. Tank turrets were removed and a fighting compartment built in their place. The earliest conversions were known as the **Nagmashot**, but these machines were soon up-armoured and converted into a model known as the **Nagmachon**. The Nagmachon is perhaps the most familiar of the IDF's LIC carriers. The Nagmachon low intensity conflict (LIC) carrier is optimised to survive hits from RPG warheads and improvised explosive devices. The machine is heavily armoured using both passive armour packages and explosive reactive armour modules. In recent years superstructures of various types have been added to the top of the fighting compartment. The Nagmachon with these superstructures has the nickname **Nagmachon Mifleset** (Monster).

The latest IDF heavy carrier built upon redundant Centurion tank hulls is the **Nakpadon**. Whilst the earlier machines relied on explosive reactive armour, the Nakpadon uses a more sophisticated armour array. This consists of a hybrid, using advanced passive armour integrated with some explosive reactive armour. The Nakpadon is intended for low intensity operations. It is thought to have the best ballistic protection of all the Centurion based carriers.

The initial Centurion based combat engineer vehicle was also the **Nagmashot**, however this was followed in the early 1990s by the Puma, the IDF's premier CEV.

In order to create a **Puma** in the ealry 1990s the turret of the Centurion is removed and a new compartment for carrying combat engineers is built within the hull. Additional armour packages are provided for the new machine. The Puma can deploy a wide range of engineering equipment ranging from a dozer blade to mine clearing devices.

Die Erfahrungen des Libanon-Krieges von 1982 zeigten sehr deutlich, dass ein in einer Gefechtszone überlebensfähiges, stark gepanzertes Fahrzeug für die Kampfpioniere und die Infanterie unabdingbar geworden war.

Der Kampfpanzer Centurion sollte in den späten 1980er Jahren das Ende seiner aktiven Laufbahn erreichen und somit die Basis dieser neuen Fahrzeugfamilie bilden.

In den frühen 1980er Jahren, nach dem Libanon-Krieg von 1982, kam somit eine Gruppe von gepanzerten Fahrzeugen auf Centurion Basis zum Einsatz, die am besten als Sturm/ Schützenpanzer zu bezeichnen sind und hinsichtlich Aufgaben im Kampf gegen Milizen in bebauten Gebieten optimiert wurden. Alle diese Fahrzeuge basierten auf Centurion Wannen, denen der Turm entfernt wurde.

*Der erste Umbau dieser Art war der **Nagmashot**. Er bewährte sich jedoch nur bedingt und wurde bald zum **Nagmachon** aufgerüstet und stärker gepanzert. Der Nagmachon ist auf Überlebensfähigkeit hinsichtlich RPG-Panzerfäusten und Sprengladungen optimiert und führt dazu eine Mischung aus passiver und reaktiver Panzerung. In den letzten Jahren wurden vermehrt Nagmachon mit turmartigen Aufbauten gesichtet, die den Namen **Nagmachon Mifleset** (Ungetüm) tragen.*

*Der modernste der Sturm/Schützenpanzer ist der **Nakpadon**, der gegenüber der Reaktivpanzerung seiner Vorgänger nun modernste Panzerungselemente mit sich führt. Für den Einsatz in den asymmetrischen Konflikten niedriger Intensität wird der Nakpadon als idealste Lösung aufgrund seiner Panzerung angesehen.*

*Die erste Variante eines Pionierpanzers war ebenfalls der **Nagmashot**, der Anfang der 1990er Jahre seinen Nachfolger im Pionierpanzer Puma erhalten sollte.*

*Auch für den **Puma** wurde der Centurion Turm entfernt und ein Kampfraum für die aufgesessenen Pioniere in der Centurion Wanne geschaffen. Zusätzlicher Panzerschutz wurde durch Zusatzpanzerungselemente außen am Fahrzeug ermöglicht. Der Puma kann eine große Bandbreite moderner Pioniergeräte, wie Räumschaufeleinrichtungen oder Minenräumsysteme, am Bug aufnehmen.*

The IDF's premier armoured engineer vehicle, the Puma, is based on the hull of the Centurion main battle tank with the turret removed. Among many other modifications the Merkava-type suspension and side-skirts, the large mounts for the various engineer equipment on the hull bow (here for the massively built hydraulically powered attachment point for a Nochri -Stranger- mine roller) and the stowage baskets above the engine deck become apparent. Note also the the the heavy appliqué armour that has been attached to the original Centurion hull and the OWS overhead weapons station here covered in plastic against the dust. Half way along the side, above the fifth road wheel from the vehicle's front, there is a folding step which can be lowered to assist passengers in debussing from the vehicle. The tactical device to the right is the symbol used for the Handasa Kravit the IDF's Combat Engineers.

Der eigentliche Pionierpanzer der IDF, der Puma, basiert auf einer Kampfpanzer Centurion Wanne von der der Turm entfernt wurde. Neben zahlreichen weiteren Modifikationen stechen am Puma besonders die Merkava-Seitenschürzen und Federung, sowie die massiven Halterungen für verschiedenes Pioniergerät am Bug (hier für den Nochri -Fremder- Minenroller) hervor. Auf dem Motordeck sind zusätzliche Staukörbe zu erkennen. Auf der Bugplatte ist eines der zusätzlichen Panzerungsmodule montiert. Als Hauptbewaffnung führt der Puma eine OWS Waffenstation, die hier zum Schutz gegen Witterungseinflüsse mit einer Plastikfolie abgedeckt ist. Über der fünften Laufrolle ist am Wannenoberteil ein klappbarer Tritt zu erkennen, der das Auf- und Absitzen erleichtern soll. Das geführte taktische Zeichen am Fahrzeug ist das der israelischen Sturmpioniere Handasa Kravit. (Author)

These photos show the cluttered appearance of the Puma's roof. As the engine is rear mounted, there is no rear access hatch for the vehicle's passengers. They have to disembark after climbing out of roof hatches. The engine deck is that of the genuine Centuion main battle tank, although many details, including the exhaust system, had to be altered, to accomodate numerous specialised equipment.
Diese beiden Fotos zeigen die unübersichtliche Oberseite des Puma. Da sich der Motor hinten befindet, konnten keine rückseitigen Zugangsluken für die Besatzung geschaffen werden. Auf- und Absitzen erfolgt somit über die Fahrzeugoberseite über Dachluken. Das Motordeck ist immer noch das des alten Centurion Kampfpanzers, obwohl zahlreiche Details, wie die Auspuffanlage, aufgrund des umfangreichen neuen Austattungsmaterials, neu angeordnet werden mussten. (Author)

These two **Puma** combat engineer vehicles have been fitted with a hydraulically actuated dozer blade, useful for clearing obstacles such as road blocks when under fire.
Diese beiden Puma sind mit hydraulischen Räumschaufeleinrichtungen ausgestattet, die sich im Einsatz zur Räumung von Hindernissen, wie zum Beispiel Straßensperren, auch unter feindlichem Feuer bewährt haben. (Author)

Around 2005, some Pumas were given an armour upgrade package for use during the Palestinian Intifada. The upgrade incorporated bar armour, designed to destroy the fuses of RPG type anti-tank warheads. The bar armour was fitted around the vulnerable engine compartment and below the side skirts to extend the protectet area downwards. In addition to the bar armour add-on armour components were also fitted on each side of the crew´s fighting compartment.

Etwa im Jahre 2005 wurden einige Puma nachgerüstet, um speziell während der palästinensischen Intifada eingesetzt zu werden. Die Kampfwertsteigerungsmaßnahme umfasste eine Zusatzpanzerung aus Stahlstäben, die besonders gegen Treffer mit RPG-Panzerfäusten effektiv war, und die um den verwundbaren Motorraum herum sowie zur Verlängerung der Seitenschürzen nach unten angebracht wurde. Zusätzlich wurden weitere Panzerungselemente seitlich am Kampfraum der Besatzung befestigt. (**Author**)

The missing side skirt and the view from the rear allow a glimpse of the suspension system. It is clear that this Puma, like other late model variants of the machine, has had the original Centurion suspension replaced with that of the Merkava 2.
Die fehlende Seitenschürze und der Blick von hinten zeigen deutlich, dass die späten Varianten des Puma nicht mehr die Federung des Centurion Kampfpanzers sondern die des Kampfpanzers Merkava 2 führen. (Author)

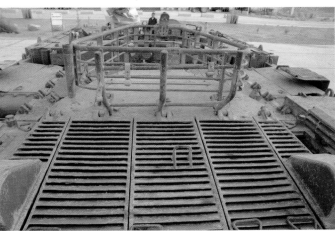

View from the rear onto the engine deck with closed and open engine access hatch.
Blick über das Fahrzeugheck auf das Motordeck mit geschlossener und offener Motorzugangsluke. (Author)

Puma from the front side. Note the IMI CL-3030 smoke grenade launcher pods at the front sides of the vehicle. The Rafael overhead weapon system is shrouded in a plastic bag. The driver's hatch is open.
Der Puma in der Ansicht von vorne. Man beachte die IMI CL-3030 Nebelmittelwurfanlage auf den Kettenblechen und die Rafael OWS Waffenstation oben auf der Wanne. Die Fahrerluke ist geöffnet. (Author)

The rear hull with the spare tracklink mounts.
Das Wannenheck mit den Halterungen der Ersatzkettenglieder. (Author)

A Puma dragging a section of an assault bridge through the sand. No information has been released by the IDF as to the Puma´s record in combat. It is known that the vehicle played a major part in the war against south Lebanese Hezbollah strongpoints.
Ein Pionierpanzer Puma mit einer Sturmbrücke im Schlepp. Bisher wurden über den Erfolg des Puma im Gefecht keinerlei Informationen veröffentlicht. Es heißt jedoch, dass das Fahrzeug einen wichtigen Anteil beim Kampf um Stützpunkte der Hisbollah Milizen im Süd-Libanon hatte.
(Author)

A Puma preparing to tow a section of an assault bridge after it has been unloaded form the two-axle four-wheel trailer visible on the opposite page center. Assault bridges are one of the main tools in use by IDF combat engineers. The photo opposite center shows one common type of assault bridge used at the IDF Engineer School in the Negev desert.

Ein Puma bei der Vorbereitung einen Teil der Sturmbrücke zu ziehen. Diese Art von Sturmbrücken bilden einen wichtigen Teil der Ausrüstung der Pioniere der Israelischen Armee. Links unten ist eine dieser Brücken abgesetzt im einsatzbereiten Zustand zu sehen, gegenüberliegende Seite Mitte noch verlastet auf einem Zwei-Achs Vier-Rad Anhänger.
(Author)

This combat engineer armored assault vehicle Puma is fitted with the RKM Nochri mine roller system and the Carpet minefield breaching system. The prime function of the Puma is to clear routes through minefields. Note in the background an open Carpet on another Puma.

Puma is the acronym for Poretz Mokshim Handasati, that means breakthrough mine engineer vehicle.

Dieser Pionierpanzer Puma ist mit einem Nochri RKM Minenroller und dem Carpet Minenräumgerät zum Schlagen von Breschen ausgerüstet. Die Hauptaufgabe des Puma liegt im Räumen von Minenfeldern und dem Markieren von freien Fahrwegen für nachfolgende Panzereinheiten. Man beachte im Hintergrund einen weiteren Puma mit nach oben offenem Carpet.

Puma ist ein Akronym für "Poretz Mokshim Handasati", was frei übersetzt etwa "Minen-Pionierfahrzeug für den Durchbruch" bedeutet.
(Author)

The bulky box carried externally to the rear hull of the Puma is the container for the Carpet minefield breaching system. This fires rockets which release a fuel-air explosive aerosol over a targeted minefield. The resultant explosion detonates the mines below and clears a safe passage.

Nahaufnahme der großen Metallbox am Heck des Puma - dem Carpet System. In diesem Behälter befinden sich Raketen, die über dem anvisierten Minenfeld ein Sprengmittel-Aerosol ausbringen, was bei Detonation die darunter befindlichen Minen auslöst und so zur Explosion bringt. (Author)

The Carpet, here seen on the same Puma from the rear, is operated remotely from inside the vehicle´s compartment. For minefield breaching, up to twenty 265mm rockets are fired in a rapid sequence over the Puma's hull.
Das Carpet-System, hier am gleichen Puma wie zuvor montiert, wird vom Fahrzeuginneren aus ferngesteuert. Um ein Minenfeld zu räumen, werden bis zu 20 Raketen im Kaliber 265 mm in schneller Folge nach vorne hin abgefeuert. (Author)

The Nochri is based upon the Soviet KMT-5 system but offers better performance. The system consist of twin trackwidth rollers, each consisting of two banks suspended from pusher bars.

Das Nochri basiert auf dem sowjetischen KMT-5 System jedoch mit besseren Leistungsparametern. Das System besteht aus zwei Minenrollern in Kettenbreite, die jeweils an einem absenkbaren Arm montiert sind.

(Author)

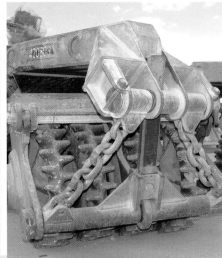

A clear shot of the Puma fitted with the Nochri mine roller. Note the massive mounts built to resist the blast of an anti-tank mine.
Vorderansicht des Puma mit Nochri Minenrollern. Man beachte die massive Auslegung der Hebe-Arme, die der Detonation einer Panzermine widerstehen müssen. (Author)

Night-time shot in a maintenance facility allowing a closer look onto this Puma without side-skirts fitted. The Merkava-type suspension with the large coil-spings is clearly visible.
Abendaufnahme aus einem Depot. Die fehlenden Seitenschürzen an diesem Puma erlauben einen guten Blick auf das Merkava-Fahrwerk mit den typischen Spiralfedern. (Author)

This Nagmashot, the original Centurion based carrier, prior to the conversion into a Nagmachon. It will receive a larger fighting compartment and a much heavier armour array.
Die Ursprungsvariante eines Sturm/Schützenpanzers auf Centurion Fahrgestell für die Israelische Armee - der Nagmashot. Aus ihm sollte bald der Nagmachon werden, der einen größeren Kampfraum und eine stärkere Panzerung besitzt. (IDF)

The heavily armored front of the Nagmachon. Note the explosive reactive armour blocks on the glacis and the open but partially armoured fighting compartment for mounted combat. The different combat role when compared to the Puma is obvious!
Die stark gepanzerte Front des Nagmachon. Man beachte die Reaktivpanzerungsblöcke auf der Bugplatte und den gepanzerten, aber teilweise offenen Aufbau für den aufgesessenen Kampf der Besatzung. Der Unterschied im Auftrag zum Puma ist deutlich erkennbar! (Marsh Gelbart)

The Nagmachon was designed as a counter insurgency platform and is a heavily converted Centurion hull. The front and rear view allows a direct comparison to the Nagmashot and the Puma. Note the massive armoured side skirts and the extensive armour plating to protect the engine compartment and mounted infantry. The raised but open superstructure allows a good situational awareness for the crew - one of the vital factors in urban warfare. However, in narrow built-up areass the unarmoured top makes the Nagmachon highly vulnerable to small arms fire and Molotov-cocktails thrown from above. A number of machinegun-mounts as well as the IS-10 smoke grenade launcher pods can be identified.

Der Nagmachon wurde entwickelt, um im asymmetrischen Gefecht als stark gepanzertes Fahrzeug seiner Besatzung erweiterten Schutz zu geben. Der Nagmachon basiert wie auch der Nagmashot und der Puma auf dem Fahrgestell des Kampfpanzers Centurion. Die Front und Heckansicht erlaubt einen direkten Vergleich zu den beiden anderen Typen. Man beachte die extrem gepanzerten Seitenschürzen sowie die Panzerplatten am Heck, die den Motorraum und aufgesessene Infanterie schützen sollen. Die erhöhte Wannenmitte mit dem Panzeraufbau ist nach oben ganz sowie seitlich teilweise offen und bietet somit einen guten Überblick auf dem Gefechtsfeld - einer der Kernfaktoren im Kampf in bebautem Gelände. Diese Art der Auslegung zeigt jedoch auch schwerwiegende Nachteile, sollte man in enge Straßen geraten und der Gegner somit in Wurfweite von Brandflaschen oder Möglichkeiten der direkten Schussabgabe von oben erhalten. Gut zu erkennen sind auch zahlreiche MG-Halterungen sowie die IS-10 Nebelmittelwurfanlage.

(Marsh Gelbart)

As with the Puma, the Nagmachon can be equipped with several engineering devices including the Nochri anti-mine system.
Wie auch der Puma kann der Nagmachon mit mehreren verschiedenen Pioniergerätschaften bestückt werden. Im hier abgebildeteen Falle ein Nochri Minenroller.
(Marsh Gelbart)

Rear of a Nagmachon with the side-skirt sections swung up to provide improved protection for soldiers intending to leave the vehicle under fire.
Der Nagmachon von der Heckseite gesehen. Die Panzerplatten der Seitenschürzen sind nach oben fixiert worden, um den Panzerschutz der auf- und absitzenden Soldaten in feindlichem Feuer zu verbessern.
(Marsh Gelbart)

The Nagmachon is equipped with IS-10 grenade launchers. These contain ten grenades each of the CL-3030 type smoke grenades. Note the extremely heavy hinges for the sideskirts.
Der Nagmachon ist mit der IS-10 Nebelmittelwurfanalage ausgestattet. Jeder dieser Container enthält zehn Cl-3030 Rauchgrananten. Man beachte auch die extrem massiven Halterungen der Seitenschürzen.
(Marsh Gelbart)

This impressive version of the Nagmachon is named Mifletset, or Monster. The vehicle is optimised for low intensity conflicts in urban environments. This machines are heavily involved in anti-guerrilla operations within Lebanon and Gaza. It is known that Hezbollah milita fighters destroyed a Nagmachon in 1996 using an improvised roadside bomb of around 100 kg of explosive. *Diese beeindruckende Variante des Nagmachon ist der Mifleset (Ungetüm). Das Fahrzeug wurde durch den zusätzlichen Aufbau für den Kampf in eng bebautem Gebiet besonders zugeschneidert. Fahrzeuge dieser Bauart sind besonders in den Einsätzen im Gaza-Streifen oder im Süd-Libanon zu sehen. Es wurde bekannt, dass Hisbollah Milizen 1996 einen Nagmachon mit einer 100 kg schweren versteckten Ladung ausschalten konnten. (Marsh Gelbart)*

In comparison to the previously illustrated vehicle this Nagmachon Mifleset has been fitted with the massive side skirts normally carried by the vehicle. The rods sticking out from the vehicles superstructure are used to attach explosive reactive armour modules.
Im Gegensatz zum Nagmachon Mifleset auf der vorherigen Seite sind an diesem nun die standardmäßigen Seitenschürzen montiert. Die kleinen Stäbe überall am Fahrzeug dienen zur Aufnahme der Module der Reaktivpanzerung. (**Author**)

The left side view, too, gives an indication as to just how thick the side skirts are.
Auch die Ansicht von links zeigt deutlich die Dicke der Seitenschürzen an. (**Author**)

The left and right rear view of the same vehicle as on the previous page.
Die linke und rechte Heckansicht des gleichen Fahrzeugs wie auf der gegenüberliegenden Seite. (Author)

Note how the rear portion of the side skirts can be raised, although leaving the suspension vulnerable, the skirts provide some protection for infantry debussing from hull hatches.
In der Seitenansicht sind gut die hinteren Heckschürzen zu erkennen, die zum Schutz der Infanterie nach oben geklappt bleiben. (Author)

The gill-like ridges found on the flanks of the Nagmachon are used to attach appliqué armour modules.
Die Halterungen am unteren Teil des neuen Aufbaus dienen zur Aufnahme von Zusatzpanzerungsmodulen. (Author)

A close-up of the vision blocks, with mesh-wire screening against thrown objects, and firing ports found on the vehicles "medieval" superstructure. The rods are associated with attaching explosive reactive armour modules.
Detailaufnahme der Panzerglas-Sichtblöcke, mit Gittermaterial gegen Wurfgeschosse, und der Schießluken am schon fast "mittelalterlich" wirkenden Aufbau des Mifleset. Die kleinen Haltestäbe dienen wiederum zur Aufnahme der Reaktivpanzerungsblöcke. (Author)

The Nagmachon has been converted to Mifleset standard with the typical raised fighting compartment with the superstructure added to the roof.
Der Nagmachon wurde zum Mifleset durch die Montage des neuen Aufbaus auf dem Dach des bisherigen Kampfraums. (Author)

Rear view of the "medieval tower" construction. The Mifleset is particularly useful in urban settings when fighting lightly armed guerrillas. The superstructure contains vision blocks and firing ports, thus allowing permanent mounted infantry combat.
Heckansicht des "mittelalterlichen Turmes". Der Mifleset zeigte sich beim Kampf in eng bebautem Gelände als besonders wirkungsvoll. Der Panzeraufbau erlaubt der aufgesessenen Infanterie die kontinuierliche Gefechtsführung unter vollem Panzerschutz durch die Panzerglasscheiben und Schussmöglichkeiten von innen nach außen. (Author)

Impressive view of the Nagmachon Mifleset. Because of the exposure of the crew to enemy fire, the Nagmachon was equipped with a notable pillbox. This protects the crew in booby-trapped areas and against sniper fire.
Der beeindruckende Nagmachon Mifleset von vorne. Die Besatzung ist im Einsatz immer direktem Feuer ausgesetzt. Nur durch den neuen hohen Panzeraufbau wird die Gefahr in vermintem Gebiet und gegen Scharfschützen minimiert. (Author)

Within the Israeli Army, no vehicle seems to be alike! This Nagmachon Mifleset has had a different style, somewhat smaller "dog house" superstructure fitted to the top of its fighting compartment. Note that the vehicles has just been completely repainted.
Innerhalb der israelischen Armee scheint kein Fahrzeug dem anderen zu gleichen! Dieser Nagmachon Mifleset hat einen etwas anders gestalteten Aufbau als das Fahrzeug, das zuvor vorgestellt wurde. Man beachte, dass das Fahrzeug gerade komplett neu lackiert wurde. (**Author**)

The Nagmachon Mifleset from the front and from the rear, this time with the reactive armour set fitted, ready for action.
Der Nagmachon Mifleset in der Ansicht von vorne und hinten, diesmal jedoch mit den Blöcken der reaktiven Panzerung montiert und fertig zum Einsatz.
(Paulus v. Wijk)

Mounted on the engine deck the mast used to jam electronic signals intended to detonate improvised explosive devices such as road side bombs.
Montiert auf dem Motordeck - der Mast für die elektronische Ausrüstung, die ferngesteuerte Minen und Bomben vorzeitig auslösen soll.
(Paulus v. Wijk)

The flanks of the Nagmachon Mifleset superstructure have been fitted with Blazer explosive reactive armour bricks. Note the substantial attachment points for the heavy side skirts which may employ explosive reactive armour to increase protection. On the upper right of the photo can be seen the rectangular smoke grenade launcher.
Die Seiten des Aufbaus des Nagmachon Mifleset sind mit Blazer Reaktivpanzerungsblöcken zusätzlich verstärkt worden. Man beachte die schweren Scharniere der Seitenschürzen, die ebenfalls Reaktivpanzerungselemente beinhalten könnten. Rechts oben im Bild die rechteckige Nebelmittelwurfanlage.
(Paulus v. Wijk)

A close up of the machine's heavy side skirts.
Nahaufnahme der Seitenschürzen vorne rechts. (Paulus v. Wijk)

Looking down to the driver's hatch. Note the vision blocks and explosive reactive armour bricks.
Blick von oben auf die Fahrerluke. Man beachte die Periskope und die Reaktivpanzerungsblöcke.
(Paulus v. Wijk)

Nagmachon Miflesets in combat. Two Nagmachon carriers support a group of Merkava MBTs in action along the border between Israel and Gaza.
Gepanzerte Sturm/Schützenpanzer Nagmachon Mifleset im Kampfeinsatz. Zwei der Nagmachon unterstützen einen Zug Kampfpanzer Merkava an der Grenze zwischen Israel und Gaza. (Government Press Office Moshe Milner)

Successor and predecessor in direct comparison: Nakpadon (left) and the Nagmashot (right). The Centurion based Nakpadon is the best protected of the IDF's low intensity warfare carriers. A useful recognition point are the ribbed appearance of its massively constructed side skirts and the lower but much bulkier armoured superstructure. As with the Nagmachon, the Nakpadon's rearmost sections of the side skirts are lighter and are often carried locked in a vertical position, thus protecting troops disembarking from the rear roof hatch.
Nachfolger und Vorgänger im direkten Vergleich: Der Nakpadon (links) und der Nagmachon (rechts). Der ebenfalls auf dem Centurion basierende Nakpadon ist das am besten geschützte Fahrzeug der Sturm/Schützenpanzer auf Centurion-Wanne der israelischen Streitkräfte und wurde besonders für den Kampf gegen Milizien und irreguläre Kombatanten gebaut. Ein gutes Unterscheidungsmerkmal beider Fahrzeuge ist das waschbrettähnliche Erscheinungsbild der Seitenschürzen des Nakpadon sowie dessen sehr viel massiver wirkende aber niedrigere Aufbau. Wie auch beim Nagmachon sind die hinteren Seitenschürzen des Nakpadon permanent aufgestellt montiert worden, um das Auf- und Absitzen der Infanterie zu schützen.
(Marsh Gelbart)

(Marsh Gelbart)

The Nakpadon is fitted with a heavily protected passenger compartment. Note the modular, replaceable, appliqué armour packs on the side of the superstructure. Note also the thickness of the sideskirts.
Der Nakpadon ist mit einem besonders stark gepanzertem Kampfraum versehen, dessen modulare Panzerungselemente hier deutlich zu erkennen sind. Man beachte wiederum die Dicke der Seitenschürzen. (Marsh Gelbart)

This view of the Nakpadon shows how the vertically raised side skirts and engine hatch provide some cover for troops disembarking via the unwieldy roof hatch. The Nakpadon, too, fields the antenna at the vehicles rear used to jam signals intended to detonate road side bombs.
Die Heckansicht zeigt gut die hochgeklappten Seitenschürzen die Schutz für die Infanterie garantieren. Auch der Nakpadon ist wieder mit der Antenne ausgestattet, die Funksignale zu eventuellen Sprengkörpern am Straßenrand stören soll. (Marsh Gelbart)

M60 MAGACH

Main Battle Tank
Kampfpanzer

The M48/M60 family of U.S.-manufactured tanks are known in IDF service as the Magach. The Magach entered service with the Israelis in the mid 1960s to replace the ageing Sherman tanks and to supplement the Centurion.

From the onset the tank was subject to a complex series of upgrades which improved firepower, survivability and mobility. The most important upgrades involved standardising on a 105mm gun, the fitting of sophisticated appliqué armour modules and up-rating the power pack. From the 1970s the Magach tanks became the successor for the Centurion tanks In the new millenium, the Magach is slowly being replaced by the Merkava and moved from active service into emergency war reserves.

The three most important variants of the Magach still in service are the Magach 6B, the Magach 7A and Magach 7C. All are based upon the M60 or M60A1. The Magach 6B was fitted with explosive reactive armour modules. The Magach 7A was equipped with passive armour arrays. The Magach 7C was given improved ballistic shaping for its passive armour arrays.

Die amerikanische Panzerfamilie M48/M60 ist innerhalb der israelischen Armee als Magach bekannt geworden. Die Magach-Panzer liefen der Panzertruppe der IDF ab Mitte der 1960er Jahre zu, um die Sherman Panzer zu ersetzen und den Centurion zu unterstützten.

Von Anfang an wurden die Magach kontinuierlich kampfwertgesteigert, was zu einer komplexen Aneinanderreihung von Rüststufen wie die Standardisierung auf die 105 mm Bordkanone, die Anbringung von Zusatzpanzerungselementen außen am Fahrzeug bis hin zur Leistungssteigerung der Motoranlage reichte. Bereits ab den 1970er Jahren lösten die Magach den Centurion als wichtigster Kampfpanzer der IDF ab.

Im neuen Jahrtausend erreichen die Magach nun das Ende ihrer aktiven Einsatzzeit und werden durch Merkava ersetzt. Viele Magach werden jedoch als Kriegsreserve eingemottet werden.

Die drei wichtigsten, noch im Dienst befindlichen Magach Varianten sind der Magach 6B mit Reaktivpanzerung, Magach 7A mit modernerer passiver Panzerung und Magach 7C mit neuer ballistisch geformter Panzerung des Turmes, die alle auf der Wanne des M60/M60A1 basieren.

This tired Magach 6B awaits disposal having been a work horse used at an IDF training base. Note the armoured instructor's seat fitted to the turret roof. The vehicle has had its Blazer explosive reactive tiles attached to its turret but not its glacis.

Dieser alte Veteran, ein Magach 6B, erwartet sein Schicksal nachdem er viele Jahre als Fahrschulpanzer der IDF gedient hat. Man beachte den Sitz des Ausbilders auf dem Turmdach. Die Reaktivpanzerungsblöcke dieser Variante sind zwar am Turm, nicht jedoch an der Wanne angebracht. (Marsh Gelbart)

Two Magach 6B tanks equipped with Blazer reactive armor tiles photographed on the Golan Heights in the early 1990s.
Zwei Magach 6B Kampfpanzer mit Blazer Reaktivpanzerung auf den Golan Höhen in den frühen 1990ern.
(Marsh Gelbart)

This Magach 6B awaits upgrading to a Magach 7C standard. The probes sticking out of the vehicle are used to attach Blazer explosive armour tiles. The tank is fitted with a Gal fire control system and was parked at an IDF ordance base in 2002.
Dieser Magach 6B wartet darauf, zum 7C kampfwertgesteigert zu werden. Die Stäbe an der Panzerung dienen zur Aufnahme der Reaktivpanzerungsblöcke. Dieses Fahrzeug ist bereits mit dem Gal Feuerleitsystem ausgestattet. Die Aufnahme entstand 2002 in einem Depot.
(Marsh Gelbart)

A photograph of the comparatively uncommon Magach 6B Batash. Equipped with a hybrid passive/active suite, the Batash has good ballistic protection for a relatively low cost.
Der relativ seltene Magach 6B Batash, der mit einer hybriden passiven/aktiven Schutzausstattung und neuer Turmform ausgerüstet wurde und so gesteigerten Schutz bei relativ geringen Kosten garantierte.
(IMI Shaul Nagar)

A Magach 7A photographed in April 2002, on patrol outside the Palestinian city of Tulkarem, during the Intifada. The heavy rivets of the new armour on the tank´s turret sides and glacis plate are prominent.

Ein Magach 7C, aufgenommen im April 2002, auf Patroullie während der Intifada in der palästinensischen Stadt Tulkarem. Die Verschraubungen der neuen Panzerung ist an den Turmflanken und an der Bugplatte deutlich zu erkennen. (Government Press Office Moshe Milner)

A Magach 7A photographed in 2002 at Tel Ha Shomer ordnance base. Note the flat turret face and its slab-sided flanks. The heavy-duty mounting rods used to fit the armoured side skirts are exposed.
Ein Magach 7A im Jahre 2002 auf der Tel Ha Shomer Basis. Die neue Turmform ist klar erkennbar. Man beachte auch die schweren Stangen zur Aufnahme der gepanzerten Seitenschürzen an der Wanne. (Marsh Gelbart)

The Magach 7A can be distinguished from other variants by the angular appearance of its turret. Note the meteorological station and laser warning sensors on the turret roof.
Weitere Ansichten des neuen eckigeren Turmes. Hier gut zu sehen: Der Querwindsensor auf dem Turmdach.
(Marsh Gelbart)

A close up of the Magach 7A's running gear and tracks. The Magach underwent continual improvements through the 1980s. However, he Magach is slowly being moved from active combat service into emergency war reserves.
Nahaufnahme des Fahrwerks eines Magach 7A. Trotz kontinuierlicher Kampfwertsteigerungsmaßnahmen hat der Magach nun das Ende seiner aktiven Dienstzeit bald erreicht. (Marsh Gelbart)

The most modern Magach variant is the 7C with furthermore improved armour. Crewmen check out their tank before boarding. Many of the post 1985 upgraded Magach have seen combat against Hezbollah and Palestinian militias and the machines have been used as mobile pillboxes, making use of their impressive armour.

Die modernste Variante der Magach Familie ist der 7C mit wiederum neuer Art der Panzerung. Hier führt die Besatzung den technischen Dienst vor der Nutzung durch. Viele der nach 1985 kampfwertgesteigerten Magach haben Kampfeinsätze gegen Hisbollah Milizien oder aufständische Palästinenser hinter sich. Seine ausgezeichnete Panzerung führte zur häufigen Nutzung als "fahrbare Bunker". (Marsh Gelbart)

A Magach 7C in the Negev desert. The wedge shaped turret profile can be seen as can the heavy side skirts which offer considerable protection and can defeat RPG warheads.
Ein Magach 7C in der Negev Wüste. Der keilförmige Turm und die schweren gepanzerten Seitenschürzen fallen bei dieser Variante besonders ins Auge. Sie bieten besonders guten Schutz gegen Treffer durch RPG Panzerfäuste. (Marsh Gelbart)

A Magach 7C from the front-side. Note the tank has fired all of its smoke grenades, the canisters each side of the turret are empty. The Tank Crew open up their field rations in a break.
Ein Magach 7C in der Ansicht von vorne. Man beachte, dass der Panzer bereits alle seine Patronen der Nebelmittelwurfanlage verfeuert hat. Die Panzerbesatzung macht gerade Mittagspause. (Marsh Gelbart)

The forward facing chevron on the side skirts indicate that this Magach 7C belongs to second company. The two rings on the 105mm gun barrel show the machine is allocated to a brigades second battalion. The markings on the turret indicate the tank is the Bet (or B) tank of first platoon.
Das nach hinten offene "V" Symbol zeigt an, dass dieser Magach 7C zur 2. Kompanie gehört. Die zwei Ringe am Rohr der 105 mm Bordkanone zeigen die Zugehörigkeit zum 2. Bataillon einer Brigade. Die Markierung am Turm zeigt den Bet (B) Panzer des 1. Zuges an. (Marsh Gelbart)

The lower glacis of this Magach 7C has been fitted with the mounting points for RKM type mine rollers. Note the tanks secondary armament of two 7.62mm machine guns mounted on the turret. The genuine M60 tracks with rubber pads showed too much wear and tear especially in the north of Israel and have been replaced by Merkava full-steel tracks, as cleary visible here.
Die untere Seite des Bugs dieses Magach 7C ist bereits zur Aufnahme des RKM Minenroller-Systems vorbereitet. Man beachte auch die Sekundärbewaffnung des Kampfpanzers: Zwei 7,62 mm Maschinengewehre auf dem Turm. Die originalen M60 Ketten mit Gummiblöcken zeigten besonders in Israels Norden zu starken Verschleiß und sind daher, wie hier gut zu sehen, durch Vollstahlketten des Merkava ersetzt worden. (Marsh Gelbart)

A Magach 7C at speed. The appliqué armour fitted to the Magach 7C weighs between 6.5 and 7 tonnes. To compensate for the extra weight the original engine of 750hp was replaced with one of 980hp.

Ein Magach 7C in voller Fahrt. Die Zusatzpanzerung des 7C wiegt zwischen 6,5 und 7 Tonnen. Um den dadurch verursachten Leistungsverlust zu kompensieren, wurde der ursprüngliche 750 PS Motor durch einen stärkeren mit 980 PS ersetzt. (**Marsh Gelbart**)

Break in the Negev desert. Note the Magach 7C´s large stowage basket on the turret rear and the armoured sideskirts.

Pause in der Wüste. Man beachte den sehr großen Turmstaukorb an der Turmheckseite und die gepanzerten Seitenschürzen des 7C. (**Marsh Gelbart**)

In addition to the upgraded engine the suspension system was improved. As a result the machine is surprisingly nimble.
Neben der Leistungssteigerung des Motors wurde auch das Fahrwerk modernisiert, was zu einer erstaunlichen Steigerung der Mobilität führte.
(Marsh Gelbart)

Relaxing during an exercise. In a war zone such close proximity to a fuel tanker would certainly not be favourable for a tank crew!
Ruhepause während eines Manövers. In einem wirklichen Gefecht wäre eine solche Nähe zu einem Tankfahrzeug sicherlich nicht der bevorzugte Platz!
(Government Press Office Avi Ohayon)

A Magach 7C supporting infantry. Note the RKM type mine rollers mounted on the tank´s glacis.
Eine Magach 7C bei der Unterstützung von abgesessener Infanterie. Man beachte den am Panzer angebrachten RKM Minenroller.
(Government Press Office Avi Ohayon)

M60 MAGACH TAGASH TSEMED

Armoured Vehicle Laying Bridge
Brückenlegepanzer

The M60A1 AVLB bridgelayer is known in IDF service as the Magach Tagash. In a later modernisation measure the Magach Tagash has been fitted with new, tandem bridges each identical and 30 rather than 60 feet in length.

When carrying the new assault bridge the AVLB is known as the Magach Tagash Tsemed. The double bridge layout gives greater tactical flexibility. The tandem bridge system is more suitable for the terrain that IDF armour operates over, which has few wide obstacles to cross, but with many narrow but deep wadis.

Der Brückelegepanzer M60A1 AVLB ist innerhalb der israelischen Armee als der Magach Tagash eingeführt worden, wurde aber später mit einer neuen Tandem-Brücke aus zwei 9.15 m langen Segmenten anstatt der früheren 18.30 m langen einteiligen Brücke kampfwertgesteigert.

In diesem Rüststand erhielt der Magach Tagash die neue Bezeichnung Magach Tagash Tsemed. Das neue Brückenlegesystem erlaubt eine größere Flexibilität und ist dem Gelände, in dem die IDF operiert, besser angepasst. Dort hat man kaum große Strecken zu überbrücken, eher aber kleinere Hindernisse wie z.B. ausgetrocknete Flußläufe.

This photo gives some idea of how awkward it can be for the machine's driver, with his restricted vision, to manoeuvre the Magach Tagash Tsemed bridge layer.
Dieses Bild gibt einen Eindruck davon, wie schwer es für einen Fahrer sein kann, ein unübersichtliches Fahrzeug wie den Magach Tagash Tsemed zu steuern. (Author)

This view of a Magach Tagash Tsemed shows the hydraulic boom mechanism for launching a bridge raised into a vertical position. Like all known IDF AVLBs based on the M48/M60 Patton family, the bridgelayer appears to be constructed around the hull of an M60A1 - note the flat and angular lower glacis.
Die Vorderansicht des Magach Tagash Tsemed zeigt den eindrucksvollen Hydraulikausleger der benötigt wird, um die Brücke auszulegen. Wie alle Brückenlegepanzer der IDF basiert dieser auf der M60A1 Wanne, die gut durch den spitz zulaufenden Bug vom M48 zu unterscheiden ist. (Author)

This view of the same vehicle shows M60-typical three return rollers for the track. Note the rubber rimmed road wheels appear, like the rest of the vehicle, to be well used.
Die Seitenansicht des gleichen Fahrzeugs zeigt das Fahrwerk des M60 mit den drei Stützrollen, den sechs gummibandagierten Laufrollen sowie generell eine starke Abnutzung durch regelmäßigen Einsatz. (Author)

This rear view of the Magach Tagash shows the engine radiators so typical of the M60 family. Note the Merkava tracks that were introduced to many U.S.-built vehicles as the original tracks with rubber-pads showed too much wear and tear on difficult soil, especially in the Golan Heights.
Die Heckansicht des Magach Tagash zeigt den typischen Aufbau der M60 Abgasanlage. Man beachte die Ketten des Merkava die eingeführt wurden, da die Original U.S.-Ketten an vielen Fahrzeugen durch ihre Gummipolster sehr schnell, besonders im schwierigen steinigen Gelände der Golan-Höhen, verschlissen. (Author)

The 30 foot tandem aluminium bridges which make up the Tsemed bridging system. The bridges are identical and interchangeable that means each bridge can be launched and retrieved by either end.
Die 30-foot (9,15 m) Aluminium Tandem-Brückensegmente des Tsemed Brückenlegesystems. Beide Sektionen sind identisch und können zusätzlich von beiden Seiten aufgenommen bzw. abgelegt werden. (Author)

Magach Tagash´s rear view in the evening sun when on the move around IDF Engineer School in the Negev desert in 2005. The supports for stowing the bridges on the engine decks are clearly visible.
Der Magach Tagash von hinten während einer abendlichen Fahrt durch die IDF Pionierschule in der Negev-Wüste im Jahre 2005. Die Ablage-Stützen für die Brückensegmente auf dem Motordeck sind klar erkennbar. (Author)

Magach Tagash on the move, with its impressively large sole plate in an elevated position.
Der Magach Tagash in Fahrt. Der Hebemechanismus ist hier in aufgerichteter Position zu sehen. (Author)

An impressive Magach Tagash roof overview. Note the driver´s and commander´s hatch. The vehicle superstructure looks pretty worn and appear just back from a field operation. Note also the spare tracklinks on the left front trackguard.
Ein beeindruckender Blick über die Oberwanne des Magach Tagash. Die Fahrerluke und Kommandantenluke sind gut zu erkennen. Der starke Verschmutzungsgrad deutet auf kürzlichen Einsatz hin. Man beachte auch die Ersatzkettenglieder auf dem vorderen linken Kettenblech. (Author)

A view of the commander's hatch. Unlike the U.S. original design, there appears to be a basic mount for a machine gun.
Blick auf die Kommandantenluke. Im Gegensatz zum U.S. Originalfahrzeug ist hier eine Montagevorrichtung für ein Maschinengewehr zu erkennen. (Author)

An overview looking via the engine deck and bridge support beam towards the driver's hatch to the left and commander's hatch to the right.
Blick über den Brückenablageträger und das Motordeck hin zur Fahrerluke links und der Kommandantenluke rechts. (Author)

Looking down on the drivers hatch, situated to the left, and the commander's hatch. Note the ammunition racks suggesting that both cupolas could have adjacent machine gun mounts.
Blick auf die Fahrerluke links und die Kommandantenluke rechts. Zwei Halterungen für Munitionskästen deuten auf zwei montierbare Maschinengewehre hin. (Author)

A view of the heavy drivers's hatch.
Detailansicht der gepanzerten Fahrerluke. (Author)

The elevating boom from the front showing the armour protecting the hydraulics.
Der Hebemechanismus von vorne, mit dem gepanzerten Schutz der Hydraulik. (Author)

The hydraulic boom appears to have been redesigned from the system originally fitted to the M60A1. The IDF boom appears to be more sturdy and robust.
Der Hydraulikarm scheint gegenüber seinem Original-U.S. Vorgänger am M60A1 deutlich verstärkt worden und nun sehr viel robuster ausgelegt zu sein. (Author)

M88
CHILUZ

Armoured Recovery Vehicle
Bergepanzer

The IDF uses the American M88A1 armoured recovery vehicle (ARV) based upon the M48 tank. The M88A1 recovery vehicle Chiluz is equipped with two winches, a hydraulic spade and hoist boom. Apart from some additional external stowage, the vehicle used by the IDF appears to be the same as that used in US service.

If funding allows, the M88A1 may be supplanted by a new, more capable, Israeli designed ARV built upon the Merkava chassis in the near future.

The Chiluz recovery vehicle is a full tracked armored vehicle used to perform battlefield rescue and recovery missions within Gaza, the Westbank and southern Lebanon.

Die IDF nutzt den amerikanischen M88A1 auf M48 Basis in der Bergepanzer Rolle. Der M88A1 Chiluz ist mit zwei Winden, einer hydraulischen Räumschaufel und einem Hebekran ausgestattet. Abgesehen von zusätzlichem Stauplatz an der Fahrzeugaußenseite scheint der Chiluz identisch zum amerikanischen M88A1 zu sein.

Insofern die notwendige Budget zur Verfügung steht, wird der M88A1 Chiluz von einem Bergepanzer auf Merkava-Fahrgestell in der nächsten Zukunft abgelöst werden.

Der Chiluz kam kürzlich bei Bergemissionen und Rettungsoperationen im Gaza Streifen, in der West Bank und im Süd-Libanon zum Einsatz.

The M88A1 Chiluz armoured recovery vehicle, unusually for the IDF, does not appear to be equipped with a machine gun. On U. S. vehicles a .50 Browning M2 machine gun is fitted immediately in front of the commander's cupola.
Der M88A1 Chiluz Bergepanzer im Dienste der IDF scheint, ungewöhnlicherweise, nicht wie sein amerikanisches Vorbild, nicht mit einem Maschinengewehr bewaffnet zu sein. An U.S. Fahrzeugen ist zur Nahverteidigung ein 12,7 mm Browing MG zu finden. (Author)

A Chiluz in IDF service from the front. The main hoist protrudes through the centre of the glacis, above the spade. The left hand cupola is for the driver and that on the right for the vehicle mechanic.
Der Chiluz im Dienst der IDF in der Vorderansicht. Die Hauptwinde wird durch den vorderen Teil des Aufbaus geführt. Die Kuppel links ist die des Fahrers, die des Mechanikers ist rechts zu sehen. (Author)

Unlike the Magach Tagash this Chiluz ist still fitted with the genuine M48/M60 tracks with rubber pads.
Im Gegensatz zum Magach Tagash ist dieser Chiluz noch mit den Original U.S. Ketten des M48/M60 mit Gummiblöcken ausgestattet. (Author)

An IDF M88A1 Chiluz from the rear. The hoist boom's frame dominates the superstructure. Directly below the exhaust deflectors can be seen a towing bar and towing pintle.
Heckansicht des M88A1 Chiluz. Der Kranausleger dominiert diese Perspektive. Direkt darunter sind die Abgasanlage und die Schleppkupplungen zu erkennen. (Author)

Looking along the right flank of an M88 ARV. The IDF's propensity to paint all hatch access handles and lubrication nipples in bright red is shown to advantage. Note the protrection ring on the drive sprocket, presumably an Israeli modification to prevent throwing the track under build-up of mud.
Die rechte Seite des M88A1 Chiluz. Auch an diesem Fahrzeug sind wieder alle wartungs- oder sicherheitsrelevanten Teile in Rot zwecks der besseren Erkennbarkeit gestrichen. Man beachte den Schutzring am Treibrad, vermutlich eine israelische Modifikation, die ein Werfen der Kette auch bei starkem Schmutzaufbau verhindert. (Author)

Looking along the left flank of the M88. Note the spare road wheel mounted to the vehicles rear.
Blick entlang der linken Fahrzeugseite. Man beachte die Ersatz-Laufrolle links hinten am Heck. (Author)

MERKAVA 2/3/4

Main Battle Tank
Kampfpanzer

The indigenous Merkava tank entered into service in 1979. With its front mounted engine, the Merkava 1 had a unique configuration for a main battle tank. Although a 105mm rifled gun gave the vehicle considerable firepower, the machine optimised protection and crew survivability.

The Merkava 2 entered into service in 1983 and incorporated improvements to its fire control, additional appliqué armour and a modified power pack.

The backbone of the IDF's armoured corps is currently made up of Merkava 3s. The machine went into service in 1989; around 650 are in service with the IDF. The Merkava 3 is a considerably more powerful tank than earlier variants of the tank. Its 120mm smoothbore gun, modular, advanced armour and improved power-pack make it a dangerous opponent. The modular nature of its armour allows the provision of enhanced appliqué armour packages as new material technologies become available. As well as the provision of better armour protection, rolling upgrades for the Merkava 3 have included the fitting of the sophisticated Baz fire control system.

The Merkava 4 is the latest version of the tank to go into service. The tank benefits from being fully digitalised, its combat power enhanced by an ability not only to electronically share battlefield information between crewmen, but also between tanks. With a more powerful engine, improved suspension, new armour modules, upgraded gun and fire control system, the Merkava 4 is at the cutting edge of tank design.

Der Merkava 1 Kampfpanzer wurde im Jahre 1979 in die israelische Armee eingeführt. Seine ungewöhnliche Auslegung mit dem Motor im Bug und dem besonders auf das Überleben der Besatzung ausgerichteten Panzerschutz machten ihn von Anfang an zu einem ungewöhnlichen Fahrzeug, trotz einer zu diesem Zeitpunkt nicht mehr modernen 105 mm Bordkanone.

Der kampfwertgesteigerte Merkava 2 wurde 1983 eingeführt und umfasste nun Verbesserungen des Feuerleitsystems, Zusatzpanzerungselemente und einen leistungsstärkeren Motor.

Das Rückgrat der Panzertruppe der IDF bildet derzeit jedoch der Merkava 3, der 1989 der Truppe zulief, und von dem rund 650 Stück im aktiven Dienst stehen. Der Merkava 3 ist beträchtlich kampfstärker als die früheren Varianten. Seine 120 mm Glattrohrkanone, die moderne modular ausgelegte Panzerung und ein noch weiter verbesserter Antrieb machen ihn zu einem gefährlichen Gegner. Besonders die modulare Auslegung der Panzerung macht zukünftige Kampfwertsteigerungen leichter. Daneben verbesserte die Einführung des Baz Feuerleitsystems seine Möglichkeiten im Gefecht.

Der Merkava 4 ist die modernste Variante der Merkava Familie. Ein besonderer Vorsprung dieser Variante ist das voll-digitalisierte Gefechtsfeldüberwachungssystem, das den Informationsaustausch in der Besatzung aber auch mit anderen Panzern deutlich erleichtert. Im weiteren sind die Antriebsanlage, das Fahrwerk, die Panzerung und das Feuerleitsystem auf dem modernsten Stand der Technik.

The dust on this Merkava 2 helps pick out the heavy rivets on the flanks of its turret. These rivets show that the appliqué armour packages, which distinguish the vehicle from the no longer in service Merkava 1, have been applied.
Der Staub erleichter hier die Identifizierung: Die Verschraubungen der moderneren Panzerungselemente an den Turmseiten zeigen deutlich den Merkava 2 an. Der nicht mehr im Dienst befindliche Merkava 1 hatte diese nicht. (Author)

The right side view of a Merkava 2 shows the unique external appearance of the main battle tank with the engine at the front and the wedge shaped turret with the 105mm main gun.
Die Ansicht eines Merkava 2 von der rechten Seite zeigt deutlich die besondere Auslegung dieser Fahrzeugfamilie: Der Motor befindet sich vorne und der Turm mit der 105 mm Bordkanone weist eine besondere keilförmige Auslegung auf. (Author)

The Merkava 2 turret in close up. Both of the IMI CL-3030 smoke grenade launchers, one on each side of the turret, have discharged all their grenades. The heavy rivets associated with the appliqué armour fitted to the sides of the turret are readily seen.
Der Turm des Merkava 2 in Nahaufnahme. Beide IMI CL-3030 Nebelmittelwurfanlagen haben ihre Patronen bereits verschossen. Die gut sichtbare schwere Verschraubung dient zur Befestigung der Zusatzpanzerungselemente zu beiden Seiten des Turmes. (Author)

This Merkava 2 is missing a section of its side skirts. A closer look unveils that the heavy special armour used does not extend the full distance of the skirt. Note also that the first roadwheel is a different type than the others. In comparison to the provious vehicles this tank is also already equipped with the late type of tracks.
An diesem Merkava 2 fehlt eines der Segmente der Seitenschürze. Ein genauerer Blick zeigt, dass der stark gepanzerte Teil der Schürze nicht bis ganz unten reicht. Man beachte auch, dass die erste Laufrolle von einer anderen Auslegung ist als die restlichen. Auch führt dieser Panzer, im Vergleich zu den bisher gezeigten, die neueste Ausführung der Kette. (Author)

This Merkava 2 has attachment points for engineering devices such as a mine roller applied to its glacis. Note also another, earlier, type of first road wheel, this time with holes to save on weight. The track is of the earlier type, too. The instructor's seat on the turret identifies this vehicle as belonging to a IDF training camp.

The tactical markings of this Merkava can be interpreted as follows: The three rings on its barrel indicate it belongs to the third battalion of a parent brigade. The cluster markings on its right fender, shows that it is Bet (or B) tank of fourth platoon. The cluster marking that can be seen on the cluster marking indicates that the tank belongs to first company. The equivalent first company marking for each side skirt is a large downwards pointing white chevron. On the tanks left fender, the 3 within a shield indicates a third battalion machine.

Dieser Merkava 2 ist mit den Halterungen zum Befestigen von Pioniergeräten am Bug ausgestattet. Man beachte auch eine weitere Variante der ersten Laufrolle, diesmal mit Bohrungen zur Gewichtsersparnis. Die Ketten sind wieder von der früheren Ausführung. Der Ausbilder-Sitz auf dem Dach des Turmes zeigt die Zugehörigkeit des Panzers zu einer Ausbildungseinrichtung der IDF an.

Die taktischen Zeichen sind wie folgt zuzuordnen: Die drei Ringe am Rohr der Kanone - 3. Bataillon, Symbole am vorderen rechten Kettenbleck - B-Panzer des 4. Zuges der 1. Kompanie, oben offenes "V" - 1. Kompanie, "3" am rechten Kettenblech vorne - Fahrzeug des 3. Bataillons. (Author)

A Merkava 2, its turret slewed to the side and its engine hatch open, exposing the front-mounted power pack. An armoured seat for a training instructor has been fitted to the vehicles roof. Note the large size of the stowage basket fitted to the turrets rear.

Ein Merkava 2 mit seinem Turm zu Wartungsarbeiten zur Seite gedreht. Der vorne montierte Motor ist nun zugänglich. Der gepanzerte Sitz des Ausbilders auf dem Turmdach ist ebenfalls gut zu erkennen. Man beachte die ungewöhnliche Größe des Staukorbes am Turmheck. (Author)

On this Merkava 2 the white line drawn across the top of the gun barrel can be made out. In darkness the white line gives the tank commander a better idea of where his weapon is pointing. This tactical marking has even reputedly been used, in an emergency, as an impromptu battle sight. *An diesem Merkava 2 ist die weiße Linie auf dem Kanonenrohr gut zu sehen. Bei Dunkelheit dient sie dem Panzerkommandanten einen besseren Eindruck, wohin seine Hauptwaffe zielt. Im Notfall kann die Linie auch zum Anvisieren eines Zieles genutzt werden.* (**Author**)

This Merkava 2 shows its characteristic rear clamshell hatch, left in the closed, to the right in open position. The solution to carry its own infantry inside a main battle tank is an absolutely unique approach worldwide. In recent years flexible, concertina style stowage baskets, made of steel mesh, have been retro-fitted to each side of the hatch. Note also the "ball-and-chain" armour on the rear of the turret, intended to deflect RGP hits. *Der Merkava 2 zeigt die typische gepanzerte Tür für den Zugang zum Fahrzeugheck, links geschlossen, rechts in der geöffneten Position. Diese Lösung zum Mitführen von eigener Infanterie in einem Kampfpanzer ist einmalig in der Welt. In den vergangenen Jahren wurden neue Staukörbe, die wie eine Ziehharmonika zusammengefaltet werden können, zu beiden Seiten des Hecks montiert. Man beachte auch die "Ball-and-Chain" Panzerung aus Kettengliedern, die ein Unterschießen der Turmrückseite mit RPG-Panzerfäusten verhindern soll.* (**Author**)

These Merkava 2 main battle tanks, stripped of their side skirts, display their suspension system. The massive helical springs are clearly visible. The Merkava on the top has a section of the thermal shroud which normally covers the 105mm gun missing.
Diese Merkava 2 Kampfpanzer geben durch die fehlenden Seitenschürzen den Blick auf das Fahrwerk frei. Die massiven Spiralfedern sind deutlich zu erkennen. Dem Fahrzeug auf dem oberen Bild fehlt ein Teil seiner Wärmeschutzhülle der Bordkanone. (Author)

Whilst survivability and lethality received most attention, the Merkava´s 2 mobility was not overlooked!
Trotz exzellenter Panzerung und Bewaffnung, wurde Agilität beim Merkava 2 nicht vernachlässigt! (IDf Spokesperson Unit Helena Moshe)

A Merkava 3 fitted with the new 120mm smoothbore gun and revised turret armour. The instructor's seat on its turret roof enables the IDF to train its crews with an experienced instructor being on hand to advise and grade raw crews on field exercises. This particular machine has been retro-fitted with the Baz fire control system which can be seen on the right upper turret roof.

Der Merkava 3 ist mit der 120 mm Glattrohrkanone und modernerer Panzerung ausgestattet. Dieser Merkava 3 ist wiederum mit dem gepanzerten Ausbildersitz bestückt. Diese Art der Ausbildung ermöglicht es, dass ein erfahrener Panzermann der Besatzung auch während eines regulären Manövers zur Seite stehen kann. Das abgebildete Fahrzeug ist bereits mit der Baz Feuerleitanlage ausgestattet, die rechts oben auf dem Turm erkennbar ist.
(Author)

This shot of a Merkava 3 shows the thick slab of armour which makes up the engine hatch, in the open position. The device immediately above the gun mantlet is a sensor for the Ancoram laser warning system which alerts the tank crew if their machine has been painted by a targeting laser.

Dieser Merkava 3 mit offener Motorluke zeigt gut die Stärke der Panzerung des Fahrzeugs. Auf der Blende der Kanone ist das Anchoram Laser- Warnsystem zu erkennen, das die Besatzung bei gegnerischer Erkennung warnt.
(Author)

A Merkava 3 showing the flat-sided appearance to its turret in comparison to the Merkava 2.
Die flache Turmseitenpanzerung des Merkava 3 im Vergleich zum Merkava 2 ist aus dieser Perspektive gut zu erkennen. (Author)

View of the Merkava's robust suspension system. Note the support brackets for the heavy side skirts.
Ein Merkava 3 ohne angebrachte Seitenschürzen. Beachte deren massiv ausgelegte Halterungen. (Author)

A Merkava 3 fitted with fourth generation Dor Dalet armour modules around its turret sides and now armed with the 120mm smoothbore gun. The cluster markings on the vehicles fenders indicate its position within the parent unit. The two parallel bars on the fender indicate the tank belongs to second company, the number 2 indicates second platoon. The "3" within the stylised shield shape show that the machine belongs to third battalion. Note the machine in the background has had a grill fitted over its engine exhaust; this helps provide protection when the machine is operating in urban environments during low intensive conflict situations.

Der Merkava 3 ist mit Dor Dalet Panzerungs-Modulen der vierten Generation an den Turmseiten ausgestattet und mit der 120mm Glattrohrkanone bewaffnet. Die taktischen Zeichen weisen diesen Merkava 3 wie folgt aus: Die zwei parallelen Streifen - 2. Kompanie, die Zahl "2" - 2. Zug, die "3" im angedeuteten Schild - 3. Bataillon. Man beachte, dass das Fahrzeug rechts im Hintergrund Gittermaterial über der Auspuffanlage führt, was zum Schutz gegen Brandmittel bei Kämpfen in eng bebautem Gebiet dient. (Author)

A mechanic working on a Merkava 3 fitted with Dor Dalet fourth generation armour modules. Note the tank is fitted with a grille over its air-intake to provide protection against the type of improvised weapons used in urban low intensity conflict.
Ein Mechaniker arbeitet an den Panzermodulen der vierten Generation des Merkava 3 Dor Dalet. Man beachte, dass dieser Panzer mit Gitterschutzmaterial über den Lufteinlässen auf dem Motordeck ausgestattet ist, um den Einwurf von Brand- und Sprengmittel zu verhindern. (Author)

This photo of a Merkava 3 Dor Dalet rear provides a good view of the rear of the Dor Dalet armour package and the ball and chain protection which adds protection against RPG rounds. It is worth noting that the metal bars of the turret basket are made of ballistic steel and serve a similar purpose. Even the external, collapsible storage panniers each side of the rear hatch are made up of perforated ballistic steel mesh.
Dieses Foto eines Merkava 3 Dor Dalet zeigt die Heckansicht der Panzerungselemente und Details der "Ball-and-Chain" Panzerung unter dem Turmheckstaukorb. Die Ketten, wie auch der Turmstaukorb selbst sowie die Staukörbe am Wannenheck sind alle als zusätzlicher Panzerschutz ausgelegt. (Author)

This photo shows the position of the rear clamshell hatch which the Merkava's front engine configuration allows. Initially designed to carry infantry onboard, today the hatch serves the crew to bail out of the tank with more protection than if using the roof hatches under fire.
Die Zugangsluke am Fahrzeugheck des Merkava 3 in geschlossener Position. War sie urpsrünglich für Infanterie gedacht, dient sie heute primär dem sicheren Absitzen der Panzerbesatzung unter Beschuss. (Author)

The clamshell door open. The tactical markings show the tank to be Aleph (or A) tank of first platoon. The usual company bar markings on the rear fender are replaced with a company name, in this case a stylised Hebrew word for the planet Venus.
Die Luke in geöffneter Position. Die Markierungen dieses Panzers zeigen sich wie folgt: A (Aleph) Panzer des 1. Zuges. Die üblichen Kompanie-Streifen am Heck sind hier durch den Namen der Kompanie in Hebräisch ersetzt worden, in diesem Falle das stilisierte hebräische Zeichen für den Planeten Venus. (Author)

A Merkava 3 with fourth generation armour modules to its turret flanks. Note, unlike earlier versions of the Merkava 3, this variant has all-steel road wheels rather than a mixture of all steel or rubber rimmed ones.
Ein Merkava 3 mit den Panzerungselementen der vierten Generation. Man beachte die hier bereits eingeführten neuen Vollstahl-Laufrollen. (Author)

A close up of battalion markings (left). This machine (right) is Bet (or B) tank of third platoon, second company. The box marked with the stylised Star of David symbol contains First Aid equipment.
Details der Bataillons-Markierung (links) und Bet (oder B) Panzer des 3. Zuges der 2. Kompanie (rechts). Der Staukasten ist mit dem stilisierten Davidstern markiert und beinhaltet Erste-Hilfe Ausstattung. (Author)

A close up of the rear turret basket and instructors seat fitted to this Merkava 3.
Details des Turmheckstaukorbes und Ausbildersitzes. (Author)

A close up of the rear upper hull - note the different design when compared to the Merkava 2.
Details des hinteren oberen Fahrzeugwanne - man beachte die Änderungen im Design im Vergleich zum Merkava 2. (Author)

Merkava 3 without (right) and with (left) Dor Dalet armour.   *Der Merkava 3 links mit, rechts ohne Dor Dalet Panzerung.* (Author)

The Merkava 4 main battle tank marked a significant technological leap forward for the IDF Armoured Corps. Wit a completely revised hull, new armour and improved engine it pushed the Merkava series way ahead of any other main battle tank in the region. The two Merkava 4 tanks here were pictured during the 2006 battles in Lebanon.

Der Kampfpanzer Merkava 4 bedeutete einen signifkanten technischen Sprung nach vorne für die Panzertruppe der israelischen Armee. Mit einer komplett neuen Wanne, neuer Panzerung und verbesssertem Antrieb bringt diese Ausführung der Merkava Familie eine neue Dimension von Kampffähigkeit in den Nahen Osten. Hier zwei Merkava 4 während der Kämpfe im Libanon 2006. (IDF Spokesperson Unit)

The Merkava 4 pushes forward, Lebanon 2006. Approximately 400 of these main battle tanks on the cutting-edge of armour technology are already in service with the IDF Armoured Corps. Aside from the completely reshaped hull front one of the key identification features are the rear sections of the sideksirts with bar-armour instead armour plate.
Ein Merkava 4 auf dem Vormarsch im Libanon 2006. Ungefähr 400 Fahrzeuge dieses neuen und technisch modernsten Typs sind bereits im aktiven Dienst der Panzertruppe der IDF. Neben dem komplett neu gestaltetem Bug ist eines der am besten zu erkennenden Merkmale der Wanne, die neu gestalteten hinteren Seitenschürzen, die nunmehr eine Stabpanzerung statt einer Stahlplattenpanzerung zeigen. (IDF Spokesperson Unit)

From the rear the Merkava 4 shows only minor differences to its predecessor Merkava 3 Dor Dalet. Note the new style tracks.
In der Heckansicht zeigt der Merkava 4 nur wenige Unterschiede zum Merkava 3 Dor Dalet. Man beachte die neuen Ketten. (IDF Spokesperson Unit)

The Merkava 4 from the front showing the completeley redesigned engine compartment now without the distinctive bulge of all its predecessors. Note also that these particular vehicles shown here all carry protective mesh-screen on all optics to prevent their damage by thrown objects during Intifada missions.

Der Merkava 4 in der Vorderansicht zeigt gut das komplett neu gestaltete Motordeck, das nun nicht mehr die typische Ausbuchtung aller seiner Vorgänger aufweist. Man beachte auch, dass die beiden hier gezeigten Fahrzeuge mit Drahtgitter über allen Optiken nachgerüstet wurden, um Beschädigung durch geworfene Objekte während Intifada-Missionen zu begegnen. (IDF Spokesperson Unit)

The Merkava 4 has a power-to-weight ratio of around 23hp per tonne, better than earlier Merkava variants. The low mobility had been encountered as one of the major drawbacks of the Merkava 1 to 3 in comparison with tanks from other nations.
Der Merkava 4 hat ein Gewichts-/Leistungsverhältnis von 23 PS pro Tonne, was ihn deutlich mobiler als seine Vorgänger macht. Die geringe Mobilität war bereits beim Merkava 1 bis 3 als größter Nachteil im Vergleich zu anderen ausländischen Kampfpanzertypen erkannt worden.
(IDF Spokesperson Unit Helena Moshe)

A line up of Merkava 4s. The distinctively shaped engine exhaust, particular to this vehicle can clearly be made out.
Kampfpanzer Merkava 4 aufgereiht in einer Kaserne. Man beachte die ebenfalls neu gestalte Abgasanlage auf der rechten vorderen Wannenseite.
(Author)

The Merkava 4's turret has lost its narrow, wedge shaped profile which made it such a difficult target to engage from the front. The new turret profile is much more bulky and similar in appearnace to the Merkava 3 Dor Dalet.

Der neue Turm des Merkava 4 ist nicht mehr so keilförmig wie bei seinen Vorgängern und nun von vorne leichter zu treffen - die neue Panzerung gleicht diesen formtechnischen Nachteil allerdings wieder aus. Der Turmquerschnitt ist weit ausladender als bei den Vorgängern und dem des Merkava 3 Dor Dalet sehr ähnlich. (Author)

This Merkava 4 has been coated with desert dust, providing a more appropriate camouflage than the standard IDF olive grey. Tactical markings show this vehicle is Bet (or B) of second platoon, third company second battalion.
Der mit Staub bedeckte Merkava 4 ist noch besser getarnt als nur in der Tarnfarbe selbst. Die Markierungen bedeuten B-Panzer, 2. Zug, 3. Kompanie des 2. Bataillons. (Author)

Through the open clamshell hatch in this Merkava, it is just possible to make out some of the ammunition stored in individual fire resistant pods.
Ein genauerer Blick in die offene Heckluke gibt den Blick auf den besonders gegen Brandgefahr geschützen Munitionsstauraum frei. (Author)

A fine shot of the Merkava 4 with its large turret slewed to the side. Note the heavy rivets which are conspicuous on the underneath of the turret and the familiar ball and chains protecting the rear of the turret against RPGs. The vertical tube attached to the turrets rear, below the instructor's seat, is the meteorological sensor mast. From this rare perspective the completely redesigned rear upper hull becomes apparent.

Ein sehr schöne Aufnahme eines Merkava mit dem Turm auf 9-Uhr-Stellung. Diese Position und der besondere Blickwinkel gibt den Blick auf die komplett neu gestaltete Oberwanne am Heck frei. Im weiteren sind am Turm der Querwindsensor unter dem Ausbildersitz, die Verschraubung der Panzerung und die "Ball-and-Chain" Kettenpanzerung gegen Unterschießen durch Panzerfäuste sehr gut zu sehen. (Author)

The Merkava 4 seen from the rear. The clamshell hatch is of a slightly different design from previous variants of the tank.
Der Merkava 4 von hinten. Die Gestaltung der Luke im Heck ist anders als bei den Vorgängern.
(Author)

A close up of the turret rear storage basket. The lower sides of the basket incorporates perforated metal armour. Unusually for IDF vehicles, the basket is protected by a close-fitting textile cover.
Nahaufnahme des Turmstaukorbes. Dessen Unterseite ist aus perforirtem Panzerstahl gefertigt. Ungewöhnlicherweise für IDF Fahrzeuge ist dieser Staukorb mit Planen abgedeckt.
(Author)

A close up of the Merkava 4's rear access clamshell hatch. The photo also shows the buckle fasteners of the turret basket cover.
Details der neuen Heckluke des Merkava 4. Man beachte die Verzurrungen am Turmstaukorb.
(Author)

This photo shows the heavily armoured maintenance hatch in the open position. The wire aerials on the front flanks of the machine are there to give the driver an indication of the machine's position in tight, urban terrain.The Merkava 4 has a different more symmetrical shaped glacis than its predecessors.
Diese Foto zeigt gut die neue Gestaltung des Bugs des Merkava 4. Die Wartungsluke auf dem Motordeck ist offen. Die Stäbe zur linken und rechten erlauben es dem Fahrer, die Abmessungen des Fahrzeugs besser einzuschätzen.
(Author)

Looking into the engine well at the gearbox of the German designed MTU MT 833 power-pack, built under licence in the USA as the General Dynamics GD633.
Der Blick in die offene Luke zeigt das Getriebe des deutschen MTU 833 Motors, der in den USA als General Dynamics GD633 in Lizenz gebaut wird. (Author)

A close up of the trainer's chair, on the turret roof of a Merkava 4.
Nahaufnahme des Ausbildersitzes auf dem Turm des Merkava 4. (Author)

The Merkava 4's turret in detail. This photo shows the new style grenade launchers, the gunner's sight to the left and the fully independent commander's sight to the right. The empty bracket directly below the grenade launchers would normally hold one of the sensors for the tank's laser warning system.
Der Turm des Merkava 4. Man beachte die neue Bauart der Nebenmittelwurfanlage - darunter die Halterung für das Laserwarnsystem, die Richtschützenoptik links und die unabhängige Kommandantenoptik rechts.
(Author)

Looking forward over the turret roof towards the 120mm gun. Directly above the gun mantle is the mounting for a 12.7mm machine gun used for training purposes. The solenoid cabling running over the turret roof is used to fire the machine gun when it is fitted.
Blick über das Turmdach und die 120 mm Kanone nach vorne. Auf der Blende die Halterung für das 12,7 mm Einschieß-MG, davor das Kabel für dessen Bedienung unter Panzerschutz. (Author)

Looking aft on the cluster of smoke grenade launchers and the gunner's sight on the turret's right side. Note the anti-slip surface of the turret roof and flanks.
Blick nach hinten über die Nebelmittelwurfanlage und die Richtschützenoptik auf der rechten Turmseite. Man beachte auch den Anti-Rutsch Belag auf allen Flächen. (Author)

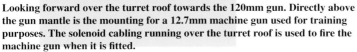

A close up of the instructor's chair and how it is fitted to the roof of the Merkava. Note the instructor has a fire extinguisher mounted within reach of his right hand.
Der Ausbildersitz und dessen Befestigung. Beachte den Feuerlöscher rechts! (Author)

Looking at the right arc of the turret from the front. The metal grill on the upper surfaces of the glacis is the air intake for the engine.
Blick auf den Turm von vorne rechts. Auf der Oberwanne ist das Gittermaterial der Abdeckungen zum Motorraum gut zu erkennen. (Author)

Finally cleared by the censor - Merkava 4's roof seen in close up. The cylindrical object directly in front of the soldier sitting in the instructor's chair, is the commander's fully independent sight. To the soldier's right, there is the commander's hatch. Note the enormously thick hatch which requires an electric motor to lift it. The rectangular box in front of the commander's hatch is the gunner's sights.
Endlich freigegeben! - Der Turm des Merkava 4 von oben: Das zylindrische Objekt rechts vor dem Ausbilder in seinem Sitz ist das unabhängige Kommandantenrundblicksystem. Rechts neben dem Soldaten die Kommantenluke - man beachte deren Dicke, die ein elektrisches Hebesystem nötig macht! Vor der Kommandantenluke die Optiken des Richtschützen. (Author)

The commander's hatch and cupola in close up. Note the vision blocks around the hatch and the massive form of the cupola and associated electric lifting mechanism. There is a mount for a 7.62mm machine gun by the side of the open hatch.
Die Kommandantenkuppel mit den Sichtblöcken und der elektrisch zu hebenden Luke und deren Hebemechanismus. Man beachte die 7,62 mm MG-Halterung vorne. (Author)

Looking directly down on to the external housing for the commander's sights.
Direkter Blick von oben auf das Gehäuse des unabhängigen Panorama-Sichtgeräts des Kommandanten. (Author)

The driver's vision blocks, which are supplemented with four cameras in armoured boxes, in an attempt to prevent blind spots.
Die Fahreroptiken die nach allen Seiten durch vier Kameras unterstützt werden. (Author)

A trio of Merkava 4s at a training base. The overhead shot makes the outline of the new turret and hull visible. Note that the road wheels of these these Merkavas have rubber rims, the same as earlier Merkava variants with the exception of late model Merkava 3s which used all steel road wheels.

Drei Merkava 4 in einer israelischen Kaserne. Die Gesamtübersicht von schräg oben zeigt sehr gut die neue Formgebung des Turmes und der Wanne. Man beachte, dass der vordere Merkava 4 noch die alten gummibandangierten Laufrollen hat, während späte Merkava 3, genauso wie späte Merkava 4, bereits Vollstahllaufrollen besitzen. (Author)

This intriguing photo shows a Merkava 4 camouflaged with fabric panels thought to have been developed by the Israeli company Fibrotex. The covering offers multi-spectrum protection, not just in the visible range, but also reduces the tanks emissions in the near IR and thermal ranges.

Dieses einmalige Foto zeigt den Merkava 4 getarnt mit den Tarnplanen, die von der israelischen Firma Fibrotex entwickelt wurden. Diese Art der Tarnung deckt nicht nur den mit dem Auge sichtbaren Bereich ab, sondern tarnt auch gegen Infrarot-Erfassung und die Erkennung durch Wärmebildgeräte. (Author)

This additional view of the Merkava 4 multi-spectrum camouflage shroud, demonstrates how it fits the vehicle's rear. The fringed material over the road wheels will help cut down on dust clouds. It is the thermal plume caused when hot engine exhaust acts on particles of dust thrown up by the tracks which are most visible on thermal imagers.

Die multi-spektralen Tarnplanen des Merkava 4 aus einer anderen Perpektive. Man beachte, wie genau die Planen auf den Panzer zugeschnitten sind. Die einzelnen Streifen über dem Fahrwerk reduzieren die Bildung von Staub während der Fahrt. Durch Abgase aufgeheizte und hochgewirbelte Staubpartikel bilden die größte Gefahr der Erkennung durch einen mit Wärmebildgeräten ausgestatteten Gegner. (Author)

D9 DOV & DUBI

Engineer Dozers
Planierfahrzeuge der Pioniere

As with any other modern Army, the Israeli Army fields numerous engineer vehicles for various purposes. This chapter is devoted to the most versatile and impressive machinery in that department - the wheeled / tracked dozers as well as combat-dozers.

The **Caterpillar D7** is an elderly machine, the last model having been built in 1961. None the less it continues to be a workhorse for the IDF, albeit in small numbers, for tasks behind the front line.

The **Caterpillar 998B** is a heavy duty wheeled loader, manufactured in the 1980s. With a totally open cabin, it has not been suitable to be put in harms way. The machine's service career has been one of toiling away on engineering projects behind the front line.

The IDF uses a small number wheel loaders, including the **Caterpillar 966G**, manufactured in the 1990s; these are the most recent of a class of wheel loaders in Israeli service. The IDF has fitted some machines with bullet-proof cabs, the windscreens of which have been protected against low velocity projectiles by wire screens. However, wheel loaders such as the 966G have never been up-armoured to match the threat level that the Caterpillar tracked dozers have been fitted to. Consequently, they are not usually used in front line scenarios.

The **Caterpillar D9 R** bulldozer is an evolutionary upgrade of the earlier **Caterpillar D9 L**. Externally there is little difference. The machine continues the characteristic "High Drive" drive sprocket configuration with its resultant triangular track layout. Like the D9 L, the D9 R is a civilian machine fitted with a tailor made armoured shell for its cabin and exposed hydraulics. The D9 R has a similar performance to earlier models and is employed in the same manner by the IDF. The Caterpillar D9 L bulldozer, usually referred to as the Cat D9 L, is a civilian vehicle which has been adapted by the IDF for military use. Various armour kits have been provided to protect the operator's cab and to shield the external hydraulics. These are thought to vary in weight from 6,000 kg to 16,000 kg dependent on the level of protection the operator requires. Equipment such as a machine gun cupola and smoke grenade launchers can also be fitted. The layout of each individual vehicle appears to be slightly different. The armoured bulldozers were originally designed for use in clearing obstacles on a conventional battlefield. In recent years they have earned political notoriety, by being used in the low key conflict between the Palestinians and Israelis. In IDF service, the vehicles are usually nicknamed the **Dov** (Bear) or **Dubi** (Teddy Bear).

Wie in jeder anderen modernen Streitkraft auch, hat die israelische Armee zahlreiche Pionier-Sonderfahrzeuge im Bestand. Dieses Kapitel ist den beeindruckendsten und vielseitigsten dieser Fahrzeuge gewidmet: Den Rad- und Ketten-Planierfahrzeugen sowie den Planierraupen für den Kampfeinsatz.

*Der **Caterpillar D7** ist ein älteres Modell aus den 1960er Jahren, aber immer noch im aktiven Dienst. Sein Einsatzgebiet liegt hinter der Frontlinie.*

*Der **Caterpillar 998B** ist ein Schwerlast-Radplaniergerät aus den 1980er Jahren. Mit seiner offenen Kabine ist es ebenfalls nicht für den Kampfeinsatz geeignet.*

*Die IDF nutzt auch eine kleine Anzahl kleinerer Radfahrzeuge mit Räumschaufelanbauten, wie den **Caterpillar 966G** aus den 1990er Jahren. Einige dieser Fahrzeug sind mit beschußsicheren Kabinen nachgerüstet worden, und an den Windschutzscheiben wurde Gittermaterial gegen Wurfgeschosse angebracht. Trotz aller dieser Maßnahmen können Radfahrzeuge bei weitem nicht so gut geschützt werden wie Kettenfahrzeuge und dienen somit eher hinter den Kampftruppen als exponiert direkt im Gefecht.*

*Der **Caterpillar D9 R** Planierraupe ist ein modernisierter **Caterpillar D9 L**. Äußerlich sind beide kaum zu unterscheiden. Beide Fahrzeuge haben das charakteristische hoch angebrachte Treibrad am Heck und die daraus resultierende „dreieckige" Auslegung der Kette. Wie auch der D9 L ist der D9 R zivilen Urprungs und wurde von der israelischen Armee mit einer Vollpanzerung der Kabine und hydraulischen Einrichtungen nachgerüstet. Der D 9 R ist in den Leistungsparametern nahezu identisch zu seinen Vorgängern und wird taktisch gleich eingesetzt. Der Caterpillar D9 L, normalerweise als Cat D9 L bezeichnet, ist ebenfalls ein Zivilfahrzeug, das von der IDF für den Militärdienst mit zahlreichen Panzerungselementen nachgerüstet wurde, um die Kabine mit Bediener und die Hydraulikanlage zu schützen. Die gesamte Panzerung liegt im Gewicht zwischen 6.000 und 16.000 kg, je nach Auftrag. Eine MG-Kuppel und eine Nebelmittelwurfanlage können bei Bedarf eingerüstet werden. Durch die Variabilität der Ausrüstung gleicht kein Fahrzeug genau dem anderen.*

Die gepanzerten Planierraupen wurden ursprünglich beschafft, um Hindernisse auf dem Gefechtsfeld zu beseitigen. In den letzten Jahren führten jedoch die eskalierenden Konflikte mit den Palästinensern zum immer stärkeren Einsatz dieser Fahrzeuge direkt im Gefecht.

*Im Dienste der IDF werden diese Fahrzeuge auch als **Dov** (Bär) oder **Dubi** (Teddybär) bezeichnet.*

Obsolete, but still useful away from the combat zone. The Caterpillar D7 in IDF service.
Zwar technisch überholt, ist der Caterpillar D7 jedoch immer noch ein nützliches Pioniergerät hinter der Front. (Author)

An IDF Caterpillar 966G wheel loader, seen in its optimum environment; working well away from the front line. The small forklift of unknown make changing the wheel of the 966 G gives a good indication of the loaders size! Note the fully armoured operator's cab additionally protected by mesh-screen against thrown objects.
Auch der Caterpillar 966 G wird im Dienst der IDF nur weit entfernt vom Kampfgebiet für vielseitige Aufgaben eingesetzt. Der kleine Gabelstapler unbekannter Herkunft, der hier ein Vorderrad des 966 G austauscht, zeigt gut die Größe des Caterpillar an! Man beachte die komplett gepanzerte Kabine des Bedieners und die zusätzliche Anbringung von Gittermaterial zum Schutz gegen Wurfgeschosse. (Author)

The appearance of the wheeled loader Caterpillar 988 B in profile, suggests its considerable power packed into what is a relatively compact frame. This 988 B demonstrates its totally open and unprotected cabin structure.
Das äußere Erscheinungsbild des Caterpillar 988 B zeigt eine kraftvolle Baumaschine an, die jedoch äußerst kompakt dimensioniert ist. Man beachte die offene ungeschützte Auslegung der Kabine.(Author)

An armoured Cat D9 L "Dubi" in all its glory. Note Caterpillar's special triangular-shaped track configuration. This is because the drive sprocket sits above the running gear with two idler wheels. This vehicle has been fitted with particularly heavy appliqué armour. Note that this Cat D9 L has been fitted with an IMI smoke grenade launcher mounted on the top rear of the armoured cab.

Der gepanzerte Cat D9 L "Dubi" von Caterpillar in beeindruckender Totale. Man beachte das für diesen Hersteller und diese Serie typische "dreieckige" Laufwerk mit dem hoch montierten Treibrad am Heck und darunter dem Laufrollenwagen mit zwei Leiträdern. Das hier abgebildete Fahrzeug ist mit einer IMI Nebelmittelwurfanlage ausgestattet. (Author)

Aside from the armoured operator's cab and engine compartment, on this D9 L Dubi, particular care has been give to shroud the hydraulic arms of the dozer blade with armour, too.
Neben der voll gepanzerten Kabine des Bedieners und dem gepanzerten Motorraum wurde bei dieser D9 L Dubi auch besonderer Wert auf die Panzerung der Hydraulikkomponenten der Räumschaufel gelegt. (Author)

Close-up of the fully armoured operator's cab. Note the open cupola on the roof. This can be used for observation or as a means of disembarking from the vehicle. Some Dubis have been fitted with a machine gun mount adjacent to the cupola. The Dubi shown here is currently being refuelled. Note the thickness of the bullet proof glass in the door!
Nahaufnahme der voll gepanzerten Kabine des Bedieners. Man beachte die offene Dachluke, die auch als Notausstieg genutzt werden kann oder der besseren Beobachtung des Geländes dient. Einige Dubis sind mit Maschinengewehren an der Dachluke nachrüstbar. Der hier abgebildete Dubi wird gerade betankt. Man beachte die Stärke der Panzerglasscheibe in der Tür! (Author)

The armoured cab design and armour to the external hydraulics of this D9 L Dubi is different to the previous machine.
Die gepanzerte Kabine und der Panzerschutz der Hydraulik ist an dieser D9 L Dubi anders als am Fahrzeug zuvor. (Author)

Dubi from the side. Although lacking the IMI smoke grenade launchers, this particular Cat D9 L has the heavily armoured cabin. Note also the louver type armour on the engine compartment´s ventilation apertures. The photo shows not just the massive dozer blade at the front, but the powerful ripper at the back. The ripper can be used to tear through concrete.

Der Dubi in der Seitenansicht. Obwohl dieses Fahrzeug hier nicht über die Nebelmittelwurfanalgae verfügt, ist es doch mit der gepanzerten Kabine ausgestattet. Man beachte ebenfalls die Jalousiepanzerung über den Öffnungen des Motorraums. Das Bild zeigt gut die schwere Auslegung der vorne angebrachten Räumschaufel und des Reißzahns am Heck, der zum Aufreißen von betonierten Flächen dient. (Author)

This photo shows the D9 L's ripper in close up. The operator's bullet proof windows at the back of the cab are also clearly seen.
Diese Ansicht zeigt gut Details des Reißzahns am Heck und der hinteren Panzerglasscheiben der Kabine. (Author)

With a weight of around 49 tonnes, and that before the application of several thousand kilograms of armour, the bulldozer has an impressive weight. No wonder the D9 L's 474hp engine is a thirsty beast!
Bei einem Gewicht von 49 Tonnen (ohne die mehrere Tonnen schwere Panzerung!) is bereits die Basisvariante mit ihrem 474 PS Motor ein Spritschlucker. (Author)

The bullet proof windows of this Cat D9 L shows the scars from impact of various projectiles. Stones, catapult pellets and possibly bullets may have impacted on the glass.
Nahaunahme der Panzerglasscheiben mit Schäden durch Wurfgeschosse oder Beschuss durch Handfeuerwaffen. (Author)

The Caterpillar D9 R, also nicknamed Dubi, is externally very similar to the D9 L in its basic appearane. Smaller dentification features include an alternate type of dozer blade and details of the engine compartment. The D9 R' s heavy appliqué armour suit is completely different to those used on the D9 Ls. Note whilst the upper surfaces of the machine are painted in IDF olive grey, the lower surfaces of the machine are still in civilian yellow. The machine has headlights mounted above its front hydraulic booms.

Die Caterpillar D9 R Planierraupe, ebenfalls mit dem Spitznamen Dubi versehen, ist in der Grundvariante äußerlich der D9 L sehr ähnlich. Kleinere Unterscheidungsmerkmale sind die Auslegung der Räumschaufel und der Motorraumverkleidung. Die gepanzerte Kabine der D9 R ist jedoch komplett unterschiedlich zur denen der D9 L. Man beachte an dieser D9 R, dass die original-gelbe Grundfarbe der zivilen Baumaschine am Laufwerk noch zu erkennen ist. Nachträglich wurden Arbeitsscheinwerfer auf den Hydraulikarmen angebracht. (Author)

The sheer size of the D9 R Dubi's landfill universal blade can be seen in this photo. Note also details of the armoured operator's cab.
Die Größe der Räumschaufel der D9 R Dubi wird hier sehr deutlich. Man beachte auch Details der gepanzerten Kabine des Bedieners. (Author)

This Cat D9 R, unlike some in IDF service has all traces of its bright yellow civilian origin painted over.
Im Gegensatz zu vielen anderen Dubis wurde an dieser das Laufwerk komplett neu in Tarnfarbe gestrichen. (Author)

The cables supplying the hydraulic boom for the ripper of this D9 R seem to be vulnerable to battle damage, in contrast to the massive armoured cab.
Die freiliegenden Hydraulikkabel am Heck dieser D9 R Dubi stehen im Gegensatz zur extrem gut gepanzerten Kabine. (Author)

The sunlight catching the universal blade of this **D9 R** give the massive machine an unaccustomed peaceful appearance. Note the unprotected hydraulic arms and the soldiers as an indicator for the Dubi´s size.
Die friedliche Abendsonne fängt sich in der Räumschaufel dieser D9 R Dubi. Man beachte die ungepanzerten Hydraulikarme. Die Soldaten erlauben einen guten Größenvergleich zu dieser wahrhaft riesigen Maschine. (**Author**)

The left side view shows the door with the massice armoured-glass section in open position.
Die Ansicht von links zeigt eine geöffnete Kabinentür mit den massiven Panzerglasscheiben. (**Author**)

There appears to be an emergency exit hatch on the top left corner of the operator's cabin.
Auf dem Kabinendach der vorderen Dubi ist eine Notausstiegsluke zu erkennen. **(Author)**

As with the D9 L the D9 R can also be refitted with additional armour protection for the hydraulic arms of the dozer blade.
Wie auch bei der D9 L kann die D9 R mit Panzerungselementen für die Hydraulikanlage der Räumschaufel nachgerüstet werden. **(Author)**

In recent years it became more and more common practice to equip those Dubis directly exposed to possible enemy RPG fire with additional bar armour. This provides addititonal protection by disabling the rocket propelled projectiles before they reach the vehicles basic armour. Lebanon, 2006.
In den letzten Jahren wurde es immer üblicher, die Dubis, die direkt feindlichem Feuer ausgesetzt sein könnten, mit einer zusätzlichen Gitterpanzerung zu versehen. Diese Panzerung lässt Panzerfaustgeschosse vor der eigentlichen Grundpanzerung detonieren. Libanon, 2006. (IDF Spokesperson Unit)

M109
ROCHEV / DOHER

Self-Propelled Howitzer
Panzerhaubitze

The IDF is a major user of the U.S. manufactured M109 self-propelled howitzer, the weapon initially entering into service in small numbers in the early 1970s.

In IDF service the M109 was known as the **Rochev** (Rider). It is almost identical to the standard U.S. M109A1 and A2s provided. Changes were limited to extra external stowage baskets.

From 1992 the IDF have been upgrading the vast majority of their Rochevs to a new standard known as **Doher** (Galloper). The Doher has substantial improvements, providing an equivalent to the U.S. Paladin upgrades for the M109. The Doher has enhanced accuracy thanks to sophisticated targeting and fire control electronics and has improved survivability.

In every major conflict of the past thirty years the M109 Rochev and Doher have played a key role in suppressing enemy movements and destroying strongpoints behind enemy lines. The recent conflicts in Southern Lebanon showed the necessity of a long-range artillery system even in assymetric warfare against militas such as Hamaz or Hezbollah.

Die IDF ist einer der M109 Nutzer mit dem größten Fahrzeugbestand diesen Typs. Die amerikanische Panzerhaubitze M109 wurde Anfang der 1970er Jahre in die israelische Armee eingeführt.

*Im Dienst der IDF war die M109 zuerst als **Rochev** (Reiter) bekannt und in dieser Ausführung nahezu identisch zu den amerikanischen Originalfahrzeugen M109A1 und A2. Lediglich die übliche Anbringung von Staumöglichkeiten außen am Fahrzeug machte eine Unterscheidung möglich.*

*Ab 1992 begann die IDF ihre Rochev auf den neuen Standard **Doher** (Galopper) zu bringen. Die Modernisierung umfasste umfangreiche Kampfwertsteigerungsmaßnahmen, die in ihrem Umfang dem U.S. Paladin-Programm nicht unähnlich waren. Die Einführung eines modernen Feuerleitsystems hat die Treffergenauigkeit und die Überlebensfähigkeit deutlich gesteigert. In jedem Konflikt der letzten dreißig Jahre haben die Rochev / Doher eine Schlüsselrolle gespielt, um gegenerische Bewegungen zu unterbinden und Stützpunkte auszuschalten. Gerade die kürzlichen Konflikte im Süd-Libanon zeigten wieder deutlich, wie ein Langreichweiten-Artilleriesystem auch zur Bekämpfung von Milizen wie Hamas oder Hisbollah herangezogen werden kann.*

A Rochev awaiting upgrading to Doher standard. The Rochev shows additional stowage baskets when compared to a "Vanilla" M109. It can be distinguished from the Doher by its 155mm howitzer´s travel lock, which unlike the Doher requires manual locking.
Eine Rochev, die darauf wartet, zu einer Doher kampfwertgesteigert zu werden. Im Vergleich zum U.S. Originalfahrzeug sind hier nur die externen zusätzlichen Staumöglichkeiten zu nennen. Im Gegensatz zur Doher ist die Rochev mit einer manuellen Marschzurrung für das 155 mm Rohr der Haubitze ausgestattet. (Marsh Gelbart)

A Rochev photographed from the left side. Note the prominent armoured housing for the fire control optics with its Television like appearance, which can be seen on the turret roof. Note that the Rochev is equipped with one external machine gun mount. The Doher carries two.
Die Rochev in der Ansicht von rechts. Man beachte den übergroßen optischen Ausblick auf dem Turmdach. Die Rochev hat nur eine Halterung für Maschinengewehre, die Doher wird später zwei besitzen. (Marsh Gelbart)

Rochev from the front. The travel lock distinguishes the vehicle from the newer Dohar, on the Rochev it is not as heavy duty, nor can it be put in place automatically.
Die Rochev in der Ansicht von vorne. Die leichtere und mechanische Marschzurrung ist eines der deutlichsten Unterscheidungsmerkmale zur späteren Doher. (Marsh Gelbart)

The stowage baskets to the rear of the Rochev's turret have in typical IDF fashion been marked with white rectangles for identification and station keeping when on the move at night. On the Doher the nearest stowage box is no longer fitted. The open hatch allows a glimpse of the ammunition stowage. By transferring equipment to the extra storage panniers and baskets, the Rochev can carry a greater ammunition load than the standard M109.

Die Staukästen am Turmheck der Rochev sind in der typisch israelischen Manier zur Identifikation und Nachtfahrt in Weiß markiert - an der Doher werden die rechten Staukästen verschwinden. Die offene Luke erlaubt einen Blick ins Fahrzeuginnere auf die Munitionskästen. Durch die Verstauung von Ausrüstung außen am Fahrzeug ist innen in der Rochev mehr Platz für die Munitionsbeladung. (Marsh Gelbart)

A Rochev from the side at the Southern Command facility. The two models of Rochev served with the artillery forces, A1 & A2, both differ one from another in some minor details. Both, as well, can be upgraded to Doher, the A5 model.

Eine Rochev von rechts, aufgenommen im Südkommando der IDF. Entsprechend der amerikanischen Vorbilder A1 und A2 unterscheiden sich die Rochev leicht voneinander. Die Modernisierung auf A5 Standard, also die Doher, kann aber für alle erfolgen. (IDF Spokesperson Unit Yiftach Ofek)

The soldiers who have painted this Rochev appear to have been a little over enthusiastic when applying red paint to areas requiring regular maintenance. Note also the black heavy duty paint and the red-on-yellow markings.
Die Soldaten, die diese Rochev neu gestrichen haben, waren wohl im Einsatz mit den Sonderfarben Rot (für Bereiche zur regelmäßigen Wartung) und Schwarz (für Bereiche mit starker Abnutzung) etwas übereifrig. Man beachte auch die Rot-auf-Gelb Markierungen. (**Author**)

This interesting photo shows a Rochev to the left and a Doher to the right. One means of distinguishing between the vehicles is that the travel lock of the Doher is of a more heavy duty construction. It can be placed into position automatically, with the crew under armour.
Dieses interessante Foto zeigt die Rochev (links) und die Doher (rechts) nebeneinander. Man beachte besonders die unterschiedlichen Rohrzurrungen, die bei der Doher deutlich schwerer ausgelegt sind und unter Panzerschutz vom Fahrzeuginneren aus bedient werden können. (**Author**)

A Rochev, the nearest machine, and a Doher from the rear. The two machines can be told apart by the rear stowage arrangements. The Rochev has a basket each side of its central hatch. The Doher only has one. The right hand basket has been replaced with a sturdy frame for mounting an external auxiliary power unit (APU).

Rochev (rechts) und Doher (links) von hinten. Beide Fahrzeuge sind gut durch die Anordung der Staukästen zu unterscheiden - beim Doher fehlen die rechten beiden, der Platz wird durch eine Halterung für ein externes Stromerzeugeraggregat eingenommen. (Author)

A Doher, hatches open, being worked on in a maintenance base at the Southern Command.

Eine Doher des Süd-Kommandos wird in einer IDF Einrichtung gewartet. (Author)

Side and rear view of a Doher in a maintenance hall. The open hatch allows a look in the ammunition stowage. The M109 Doher is equipped with external generator, this is positioned instead the right-back basket and its two external cells. The M109 howitzer works with a crew of seven.
Seiten- und Heckansicht einer Doher in einer Wartungshalle. die offenen Luken geben den Blick auf die Munitionsbestückung frei. Die M109 Doher ist mit einem externen Stromerzeugeraggregat ausgestattet, das hinten rechts in die hier sichtbare Halterung montiert wird. Die M109 hat eine Besatzung von sieben Mann. (**Author**)

The Doher (Galloper) self-propelled howitzer was introduced to the artillery forces personnel in 1993. The Doher is an improved Rochev (M109A1 and M109A2). The IDF maintenance units designed it after some combat experiences in the territories.

Die Panzerhaubitze Doher basiert auf kampfwertgesteigerten Rochev (M109A1 und A2) und wurde 1993 aufgrund von Erfahrungen in den besetzten Gebieten eingeführt. (Author)

This impressive shot of a Doher shows the length of its 155mm/39 calibre ordnance.
Totale der Doher mit ihrem eindrucksvollen L39 Rohr im Kaliber 155 mm. (**Author**)

A Doher self-propelled howitzer shwoing the back blast of its 155mm main armament during the 2006 mission in southern Lebanon.
Eine Panzerhaubitze Doher beim Abschuss während der Gefechte im Süd-Libanon 2006. (**IDF Spokesperson Unit**)

IDF Vehicle designations overview
Übersicht der Fahrzeugbezeichnungen der IDF

Achzarit
"Cruel girl", a T-54/55 based heavy armoured personnel carrier.
"Grausames Mädchen", ein T-54/55 umgebaut zum schweren Sturm-Mannschaftstransportwagen.

Bardelas
"Cheetah", the official name for the M113 family of vehicles.
"Jagdleopard", der offizielle Name der M113 Familie im Dienste der IDF.

Batash
Acronym for "Bitachon Shotef" or "Overall Security". A designation that means that the machine has been fitted with a low intensity appliqué armour package.
Akronym für "Bitachon Shotef" - "Umfassende Sicherheit". Bezeichnet Fahrzeuge die mit der Zusatzpanzerung für Konflikte niedriger Intensität ausgestattet worden sind.

Baz
The Merkava fire control system, meaning "Falcon", an acronym for "Barak Zoher"-"Shining lightning".
"Falke" - das Feuerleitsystem des Merkava, ein Akronym für "Barak Zoher" - "Greller Blitz".

Chatap
"Huliya Techint Plugatit" - "Company's technical and engineer" based M113 vehicle.
"Huliya Techint Plugatit" - "Technisches Unterstützungsfahrzeug der Kompanie" auf M113 Basis.

Chiluz
The M48 based medium recovery vehicle M88.
M88 Bergepanzer auf M48 Basis.

Doher
"Galloper", an improved M109 SPG.
"Galopper" - eine kampfwertgesteigerte Panzerhaubitze M109.

Dov
"Bear"- the D9 Dozer series.
"Bär" - die D9 Planierraupe.

Dubi
"Teddy Bear", again the impressive and heavily armored D9 dozer series.
"Teddybär - wieder die gepanzerte D9 Planierraupe.

Gimel
"Gimel" is the 3rd letter of the Hebrew alphabet. The name for the Magach 7C.
"Gimel", der dritte Buchstabe des hebräischen Alphabets. Bezeichnung für den Magach 7C.

Kasman
Acronym for "Kesem a Mangina", meaning as much as "The Charm Of Music". Improved M113.
Akronym für "Kesem a Mangina - "Betörende Musik". Kampfwertgesteigerter M113.

Magach
Acronym for "Merkavot Giborey Ha'milchama", meaning "Chariots of the War Heroes", the Israeli M48/60 based tanks. Other sources mention it as "Movil Gviyot Charukhot". Another explanation is an acronym for the three Hebrew characters Mem, Gimel and Chaf - Gimel is the first letter for the Hebrew word for Germany, whilst the letters Mem and Chaf have the numerical value 48. The designation is in honour of the fact that the first IDF's M48 tanks were delivered via Germany.
Akronym für "Merkavot Giborey Ha'milchama" - "Streitwagen der Kriegselden" - der israelische M48/60. Andere Quellen nennen "Movil Gviyot Charukhot". Eine weitere Erklärung sind die drei hebräischen Schriftzeichen Mem, Gimel und Chaf - Gimel ist der der erste Buchstabe des Wortes für Deutschland, Mem und Chaf bedeuten 48. Die Bezeichnung ehrt die ersten M48 die aus Deutschland geliefert wurden.

Maoz
"Stronghold", the improved M113 APC with a converted "Dog House".
"Festung", ein kampfwertgesteigerter M113 mit umgebauter "Hundehütte".

Merkava
"Chariot", the word comes from the Hebrew root "Resh-Kaf-Bet", meaning vehicle.
"Streitwagen". Das Wort kommt von "Resh-Kaf-Bet" - Fahrzeug.

Mifleset
"Monster", an improved Nagmachon with impressive turret.
"Ungetüm", ein Nagmachon mit komplettem Panzeraufbau in Turmform.

Mugaf
The tracked command post carrier M577.
Kommando-/Führungsfahrzeug M577.

Nagmachon
Presumably "Nagmash" and "Gashon", meaning "Armoured Personnel Carrier" and "Belly" - the Centurion based Nagmashot with added belly armour and Blazer.
Angenommenerweise "Nagmash" und "Gashon" - Gepanzerter Mannschaftstransportwagen und "Bauch". Ein Nagmashot auf Centurion Basis, der die Unterbodenpanzerung und Blazer Reaktivpanzerung führt.

Nagman
An early variant of the M113 with armoured roof components.
Frühe Variante des M113 mit Panzerungselementen auf dem Wannendach.

Nagmash
Acronym for "Noseh Guysot Meshoryan", Armoured Personnel Carrier.
Akronym für "Noseh Guysot Meshoryan" - Gepanzerter Mannschaftstransportwagen

Nagmashot
Acronym for "Nagmash" and "Sho't" (whip).
Akronym für "Nagmash" und "Sho't" (Peitsche).

Nakpadon
Centurion based APC, the heavy version with new superstructure and passive armour.
Sturm/Schützenpanzer auf Centurion Basis mit neuem Aufbau und passiver Panzerung.

Pikud
M113 signal and command variant.
M113 Fernmelde- und Kommandovariante.

Roher
"Rider" - The basic Israeli M109 SPG howitzer.
"Reiter" - Die Standard Panzerhaubitze M109.

Puma
"Poretz Mokshim Handasati", "Minefield breakthrough vehicle".Centurion based heavy combat engineer vehicle.
"Poretz Mokshim Handasati", "Fahrzeug zum Durchbrechen von Minenfeldern". Pionierpanzer auf Centurion Wanne.

Vayzata
M113 TOGA armor suite on the Nagmash armoured personnel carrier.
M113 mit TOGA-Panzerung, basierend auf dem Nagmash Mannschaftstransportwagen.

Zelda
Early and unofficial name of the M113 APC.
Früher und inoffizieller Name für den M113 Mannschaftstransportwagen.